Living with Grief
Since COVID-19

Edited by Kenneth J. Doka and Amy S. Tucci

Foreword by J. William Worden

HOSPICE FOUNDATION
OF AMERICA

This book is part of Hospice Foundation of America's *Living with Grief* series.

Ordering Information

Call: Hospice Foundation of America (HFA) at 800-854-3402

Write:
Hospice Foundation of America
1707 L Street NW, Suite 220
Washington, DC 20036

Visit HFA online:
www.hospicefoundation.org

Managing Editor: Lisa McGahey Veglahn
Proofreaders: Cindy Bramble and Joan Murphy
Layout and Design: HBP, Inc.

ISBN: 978-1-893349-19-3

Dedication

To Paul Shanahan
in appreciation of his remarkable journey
and a life in service of others

KJD

❧

For those on the front line of this historic pandemic
and for all who grieve in its wake

AST

Contents

Acknowledgments

We begin by acknowledging all of those courageously involved in the fight against COVID-19 and all of those who have been devastated by this disease during a brutal time in world history.

With this book, we at Hospice Foundation of America (HFA) hope to leave a small imprint that will be useful now and in the future, as we reflect on the pandemic's wrath and its impact on communities, health care, and grief support, while mapping our way to a better tomorrow in the wake of enormous individual and collective loss.

Many of our authors this year have been on the front lines of this pandemic, either professionally or personally. And, as we all know, the professional experience has inevitably become personal over the last year. These authors have shared their expertise and experience, their pain, sadness, and frustration, often juggling patient and family care along with our deadlines, demands, revisions, and queries. We are deeply grateful.

Special recognition goes to our managing editor, HFA's vice president for programs, Lisa McGahey Veglahn, who keeps us on deadline and carefully reviews all aspects of this publication, as well as to the book's proofreaders, Cindy Bramble and Joan Murphy. We wish to give a special thanks to Lindsey Currin, producer of the *Living with Grief®* continuing education program, which addresses the same subject as this book.

We also need to recognize our supportive Board of Directors for their tireless effort and counsel that keeps the Foundation grounded and moving forward, following the lead of the late Jack Gordon and former HFA president and current board member David Abrams, who blazed a trail worth following.

The Foundation exists through the assistance of our partners, sponsors, and many donors. We are so appreciative of their respect for our work, demonstrated by their generous financial support.

Last, but certainly not least, the editors would like to thank their families and friends, who play a significant and meaningful role in our work.

A Note From the Editors

This book is going to print at the end of a tumultuous and unprecedented year.

We have chosen to use a consistent number throughout the book for the overall cases and death rates from COVID-19 in both the United States and globally, using data retrieved on December 31, 2020. For the U.S. cases (19,663,976) and deaths (341,199), we used the Centers for Disease Control and Prevention (CDC) COVID Data Tracker. For the global cases (81,947,503) and deaths (1,808,041), we used the World Health Organization (WHO) Coronavirus Disease Dashboard. Sadly, while seeing these numbers in print is sobering, we are well aware that by the time this book is available, those numbers will have increased dramatically, and that each "number" represents not only the death of someone who was loved but is multiplied by the grief of all of those left behind.

Events of this year also served as a painful reminder of the inequities and necessary lessons to be learned as our society continues to grapple with racial injustice. For that reason, we have chosen to capitalize the word *Black* but continue to use *white* in lowercase when describing race. This seeming inconsistency came out of important discussions among our staff. The decision follows the lead of the Associated Press, considered a strong leader in determining writing style. The editors of the *New York Times* noted the distinction that "…white doesn't represent a shared culture and history in the way Black does, and also that white has long been capitalized by hate groups" (Coleman, 2020).

Finally, it is important to note that this volume reflects opinions and viewpoints that are the authors' alone, which are not necessarily those of the editors or of Hospice Foundation of America.

References

Centers for Disease Control and Prevention (CDC). (2020). CDC COVID data tracker (maps, charts, and data provided by the CDC). Retrieved Dec. 31, 2020 from https://covid.cdc.gov/covid-data-tracker/#cases_casesper100klast7days

Coleman, N. (July 5, 2020). Why we're capitalizing black. *The New York Times*. Retrieved from https://www.nytimes.com/2020/07/05/insider/capitalized-black.html

World Health Organization (WHO). (2020). WHO coronavirus disease (COVID-19) dashboard. Retrieved December 31, 2020 from https://covid19.who.int/

Foreword

J. William Worden

The COVID-19 pandemic has caused hundreds of thousands of deaths in almost every country around the world. As of this writing, almost two deaths every minute are occurring due to the disease in the United States; more than 341,000 Americans have died due to COVID-19 since the start of the pandemic (CDC, Dec. 31, 2020).

In this book the editors have brought together experts in the fields of palliative care, hospice care, and bereavement to discuss how this pandemic may affect the experience of grief for those who have lost loved ones since the pandemic began in early 2020. When I think of my own clinical experience with the bereaved during this period, at least four features of COVID-19 deaths come to mind. Each of these can present problems for the mourner that may hinder a good adaptation to the death.

The first has to do with the *suddenness* of contracting the virus and the suddenness of many of the deaths. It is not unusual for a person to be whisked away to the hospital and for the family to never see them alive again. In our Harvard University research, Avery Weisman and I found that sudden death makes it more difficult for survivors to wrap their minds around the reality of the death, which is essential to processing the tasks of mourning. You must first believe that it happened before you can deal with the emotional impact.

Adding to a sense of unreality about the death is the second feature, the *need to distance.* Family members are frequently not allowed to be at the bedside of a dying loved one. They may be able to observe their dying loved one through a window or see them on a phone or computer screen but are not allowed to hold the dying person's hand or to say their goodbyes at the bedside. This can leave mourners with considerable "unfinished business" with their loved one. Distancing can also make it difficult for family members to be together both before the death and afterwards. This reality can hinder the opportunity for touching and hugging family and friends for support, which is often a major objective of funeral rituals.

A third feature is the heightened possibility that there will be *more than one* COVID-19 related death in the same family. These multiple death losses can often create what Robert Kestenbaum calls "bereavement overload" (Neimeyer & Holland, 2006). The survivor will have experienced too much grief over a brief time span. These multiple deaths can lead to a shutdown of the grieving process and can cause the mourner to experience a delayed grief reaction or to experience grief as some type of physical symptom.

A fourth feature of a COVID-19 death that can affect the mourning process is the issue of *preventability*. Both the illness and the death might have been prevented. It is common for mourners to wonder, "If only I had…." Infection and preventability can lead to a heightened anxiety when the mourner feels he or she might become infected with the virus and possibly die. Such anxiety comes from a heightened sense of the concept of *personal death awareness* (Worden, 1976). Preventability can also lead to anger and blame toward the person or situation that caused the infection. Anger and frustration may be felt at others who did not follow the social guidelines recommended by disease prevention experts. When I see this kind of anger and blame, I am reminded of similar dynamics in the early days of the HIV/AIDS epidemic, with issues of virus transmission and preventability often leading to expressions of guilt and blame. Guilt can also be experienced as *survivor guilt*, where one may ask, "Why did my loved one die and I am still alive?"

These features of COVID-19 deaths are at the foundation of the issues discussed in this timely book. Other topics include the challenges of COVID-19 illnesses and deaths for those working in nursing homes, skilled nursing facilities, and for our many hospice and palliative care programs. Chapters also include an examination of how to reconstruct funeral rituals and find other creative ways to support grievers to help accommodate the realities of these deaths. And perhaps most importantly, this book documents what will be a much longer examination of the long-term consequences for those grieving these losses, including complicated grief and trauma reactions.

Read these chapters with interest and share their knowledge of the pandemic's implications with colleagues and friends. After all, one of the best avenues for problem solving is when bright people shine light on tough issues.

J. William Worden, PhD, ABPP, is a Fellow of the American Psychological Association and holds academic appointments at the Harvard Medical School and the Rosemead Graduate School of Psychology. He is *Co-Principal Investigator of the Harvard Child Bereavement Study based at the Massachusetts General Hospital and is the author of nine books including* Grief Counseling & Grief Therapy *and* Children & Grief: When a Parent Dies.

REFERENCES

Centers for Disease Control and Prevention (CDC). (2020). CDC COVID data tracker (maps, charts, and data provided by the CDC). Retrieved Dec. 31, 2020 from https://covid.cdc.gov/covid-data-tracker/#cases_casesper100klast7days

Neimeyer, R. A., & Holland, J. M. (2006). Bereavement overload. In Salkind, N. J. (Editor). *Encyclopedia of human development,* pp. 166-167. Thousand Oaks, CA: Sage.

Worden, J. W. (1976). *Personal death awareness: Breaking free of fear to live a better life now.* New York, NY: Prentice-Hall.

Worden, J. W. (Ed). (2018). *Grief counseling and grief therapy: A handbook for the mental health practitioner (5th Ed.).* New York, NY: Springer.

Introduction

In early 2020, we at Hospice Foundation of America (HFA) were enthusiastically planning our 2020 *Living with Grief*® program on intimacy and sexuality, a topic that we perceived as critical yet neglected. In the course of planning, reports emerged of a new virus that seemed to have originated in Wuhan, China. At the time, like much of the world, we paid little attention, figuring it would be similar to recent viral pandemics such as SARS and H1N1. While these diseases were problematic, they were more readily controlled and never had the international impact that COVID-19 would prove to have—infecting so many, killing many, disrupting everything from family life to politics to tourism to the global economy. Quickly, HFA turned its attention the COVID-19 crisis, reaching more than 33,000 viewers needing information about end-of-life care and grief during the pandemic.

We recognized that there was even more that we could do, and that it was essential to plan our 2021 conference focusing on *Living with Grief Since COVID-19*. The reasons are clear. Even as I write this introduction, with the vaccine distribution beginning, the impacts of the disease are likely to be long lasting.

The COVID-19 pandemic will inevitably lead to a consequent pandemic of complicated grief. Whether an individual has died from the disease or some other cause, every death and every grief journey has been affected by COVID-19. Visits to healthcare facilities such as hospice units, hospitals, or nursing homes have been either completely restricted or severely curtailed, often leaving people to die without loved ones present and burdening survivors with "unfinished business" and other regrets. Amid the necessary restrictions, hospice teams and other professionals have felt cut off from their calling, leaving them to despair about not being able to provide the services they pride themselves on or that their patients and families need. Healthcare workers whose contact has not been curtailed have faced their own fears and the grief of so many deaths. Social distancing regulations have limited the collective value of funeral and memorial rituals. Quarantines and travel restrictions have further inhibited the opportunities to come together either to console the dying or to mourn with the living.

Moreover, our society, as most others, has experienced multiple losses such as losses of jobs, opportunities for community and entertainment, educational options, and losses of income, to name just a few. Most seriously perhaps, we have collectively experienced the loss of our assumptive world—the view that the world is safe, benevolent, and more or less predictable. It is that loss that lies at the heart of trauma.

The chapters in this book are of two types. The scholarly contributions explore varied dimensions of this pandemic, including a chapter that compares this pandemic to others that have bedeviled societies. Many aspects of this pandemic, however, are unique to our time. Rosenblatt and Wallace explore the significant racial disparities in the impact of the disease. Leah McDonald describes the challenges that COVID-19 poses to hospice and palliative care, while Healy reviews the impact of the disease on nursing homes. Neimeyer and Lee address a series of issues as they consider the effects of this pandemic on grief and introduce new assessment tools specific to coronavirus anxiety and pandemic grief. Fink reviews the spiritual challenges posed by the pandemic.

In addition to these chapters, useful personal perspectives from a wide range of professionals continue the discussion. Mary McDonald gives her insight into the lengths that hospice and palliative care teams are going to in order to support families during a loved one's illness and death, and Kotar shares her personal and professional experience through deployments as a front-line nurse. Georgopoulos explores the new world of virtual bereavement support groups. In examining the spiritual dimensions of loss, Metzler describes how one Episcopal diocese chose to face these challenges. And Villanova shares his perspective as a funeral director serving New York families at the height of the pandemic there.

Yet this book would not be complete without hearing the sobering voices that recount the very personal impacts of the pandemic on those most deeply involved. O'Brien shares the losses that she continues to cope with as a COVID-19 long hauler, and Cidoni reflects on the heartbreaking loss of her mother, resulting in both unimaginable grief and a new sense of resilience.

As this introduction concludes, it is perhaps important to add one positive note gleaned from the first chapter. Past pandemics have devastated societies. Yet just as with the concept of posttraumatic growth (where some individuals emerge from trauma experiencing, along with their grief, a new sense of growth), past pandemics have also led to growth. Such growth has included improvements in health care, sanitation, and education. Perhaps one such growth from COVID-19 will be an increased international recognition that we are truly on this planet together. Hemingway (1929), in *A Farewell to Arms*, expressed this well: *The world breaks everyone but afterward many are strong at the broken places.*

CHAPTER 1

Setting the Stage: Pandemics as Change Agents

Kenneth J. Doka

In 1935, Hans Zinsser wrote what was to become a popular science classic entitled *Rats, Lice, and History*. His thesis was that, as much as humans liked to think that they controlled the path of history, in fact this egocentric perspective is unsupported. To Zinsser, much of the scope of human history is influenced by invisible organisms—bacteria and viruses—often borne by carriers such as rats and lice. Zinsser then describes the varied roles that past diseases and pandemics have had on world history. He reminds that battles and sieges were often not won by generals but rather victories were the results of diseases that had decimated the defeated enemy more than they had troubled the victorious combatants. The allied victory in World War I, Zinsser asserts, had less to do with allied commanders Marshal Foch and General Pershing and more to do with a typhus pandemic that both weakened the Central Powers and dissipated their morale. Everything from history to fashion was influenced by the varied parasites that troubled humanity. Engineering marvels like the Panama Canal owed as much to the conquest of yellow fever as it did to engineers. The style of wigs from Egypt to the 18th century served to control the ubiquitous lice. To Zinsser, humans simply fail to acknowledge the role of disease as a determinant of their own history.

That truly is clear as the world struggles with the pandemic of COVID-19. We certainly have seen many horrendous effects. More than 340,000 people have died from COVID-19 in less than 9 months in the United States (CDC, Dec. 31, 2020). Dying people have been separated from family, meaning that they face death in isolation. And the impacts are wide reaching. World economies have been disrupted. Schools were closed for long periods of time and many, at the time of this writing, were still offering remote or some combination of distance and in-person learning. Commerce has been disturbed. Entertainments such as film and theatre have been curtailed or closed. Restaurants have been shuttered and quarantines imposed. Historians and analysts will likely long argue about the long- and short-term effects of this pandemic on both world affairs and other events such as the 2020 presidential election.

Prior pandemics have created not only havoc but also paradigm shifts leading to significant change, sometimes even growth. Just as individual grievers can experience posttraumatic growth (Calhoun & Tedeschi, 2006), so can societies grow from such traumatic events as pandemics. Prior pandemics have led to, among other things, development of more effective health and sanitation systems as well as great strides in medicine. An exploration of the effects of past pandemics, examining both the negative and positive impacts, can help to look at what role the COVID-19 pandemic may play in fostering both change and perhaps growth.

PANDEMICS IN HISTORY

Dread Diseases

In an earlier work (Doka, 1997), I described two types of diseases historically dreaded by humans. Some dreaded diseases are those called *shameful stigmas*. Diseases such as leprosy, syphilis, tuberculosis, and cancer were feared both for the slow, painful way that persons died as well as the stigma associated with the disease. Other dreaded diseases were the *great plagues* that decimated human populations such as the bubonic plague (or Black Death), cholera, typhoid fever and typhus, and the influenza pandemic of 1918-1919. These diseases were feared for the collective devastation that they wrought, disrupting the social order and killing millions. The COVID-19 pandemic clearly falls into this category and so it would be of value to understand the impacts that these prior plagues had—both positive and negative—on the social order.

The Bubonic Plague (Black Death)

The bubonic plague, alternately known as the Black Death, represents one of the most devastating diseases to have troubled humans. The disease has two forms. The bubonic form is spread by bacteria that were carried by fleas, infecting rats. These fleas can infect humans and often did so as the rat population died from the illness. The story of the Pied Piper is a thinly veiled reference to the plague where, after the rats disappeared, the most vulnerable population—the children—were often the next victims to succumb. The other form of the disease is pneumonic, spread person to person by air droplets or spit, which is a form even more deadly.

The origins of the bubonic plague remain obscure. Some think that the plague of Thucydides may have been this plague. Others identify it as the plagues mentioned in the Old Testament that decimated the Philistines and perhaps ended the Assyrian King Sennacherib's siege of Jerusalem, though these references are highly debated (Doka, 1997). It is clear that the bubonic plague was the plague of Justinian in AD 541, which ended what was likely to be Byzantine Emperor Justinian's attempt to reconstitute and restore the Roman Empire in the West. Justinian had secured peace with Rome's old enemy, Persia, and was well poised to reconquer a West that actually longed for the peace and security of a renewed Rome. Ironically, it was the very success of Justinian's policy reopening trade routes between the East and West that enabled the spread of the disease.

The death toll was massive. Estimates are that near 50% of the population, perhaps as many as 100 million people, died (Marks & Beatty, 1976). Towns, villages, and even cities disappeared, agriculture regressed to a subsistence level, and this rising empire fell into deep decline. Moreover, health suffered as Greek and Roman medicine and ideas that were precursors to germ theory (i.e., that pathogens cause disease) seemed powerless. Instead, the disease was blamed on divine wrath, focusing on the theological disputes about the nature of Christ.

The disease seemed to have disappeared from Europe for centuries until the 1300s when it roared back from Asian reservoirs. Again, the reemergence of trade, the repopulation of cities, and refugees from Mongol invasions all had roles in spreading the plague. It is estimated that anywhere between 25-40% of the population succumbed to the disease (McNeill, 1976). Once again divine retribution was seen as the cause, perhaps for sexual immoralities or tolerating heresies. Pope Clement VI's call for a pilgrimage to Rome only served to facilitate the spread. As is often the case, blame was cast that led to the persecution of more marginal members of society of the time, including Jews, lepers, the disabled, heretics, and homosexuals.

The Black Death's impact on the social order was substantial. Hourani (1991), an Islamic Scholar, believed that the disease severely weakened the Islamic world, leading to the Christian reconquest of Spain and the Ottoman capture of the Islamic world. The impact of the disease contributed to an emergent individualism (Aries, 1987); weakened Western feudalism (Claster, 1982); and set the stage for the Reformation where the judgmental and penitential systems—a response to the plague—were challenged by Luther. The subsequent effects of the Reformation were epochal, shattering Christian unity but having wide-ranging implications including the growth of education, nationalism, and capitalism (Weber & Kalberg, 2013).

Even though the plague still exists, it remains a rare disease. We no longer accept rat and flea infestation as a normal part of existence. Evolution (which tends to favor less virulent strains) and modern medicine have reduced mortality to less than 10%, which was once the survival rate.

Cholera

Cholera came close to creating the sense of dread once captured by the bubonic plague. Cholera is caused by a form of bacteria that infects the intestinal linings. The infection results in severe diarrhea, vomiting, and intestinal pain. Death usually results from dehydration. Spread by polluted water or raw vegetables and fruit washed in such water, cholera has largely disappeared in the developed world and is generally successfully treated by antibiotics and intravenous fluids.

There were four major pandemics of the disease between 1817 and 1875. Cholera was deeply feared both for its rapid spread and quick lethality. At the time, cholera was epidemic to India, but the British colonization of India, as well as increased trade and migration, helped spread the disease.

Given the fact that cholera was spread by unsanitary sources of water, it disproportionately affected the poorer social classes. And as in prior pandemics, there were strong theological messages stigmatizing victims as drunks who were filthy and wicked (Doka, 1997). Yet rapid medical advances in recognizing the sources of illness enhanced the standing of medicine. Quarantines and sanitary cordons designed to stem the spread were both controversial and generally effective. Societally, these advances led to improved sanitation and public health as societies recognized that diseases once started in the slums rarely remained there. The cholera pandemic sparked the subsequent urban reform movement that would give rise to efforts to decrease poverty, such as public schools, as well as professions, such as the emergence of social work.

Typhoid Fever and Typhus

Despite the similarly sounding names, typhoid fever and typhus are two separate illnesses. Typhoid fever is caused by the bacillus *Salmonella typhi* found in human feces and spread by contaminated food and water. Readers may remember the story of Typhoid Mary; she was a cook named Mary Mallon, an asymptomatic carrier, who infected hundreds with the disease before she was quarantined at New York City's isolated North Brother Island. The disease creates symptoms similar to cholera, such as diarrhea, abdominal pain, and fever. Typhus, on the other hand, is caused by *rickettsia* or *orientia* bacteria. Like the plague, it is spread by fleas directly or infected rats; symptoms include fever, violent headaches, and rashes.

While the diseases are dissimilar in many ways, both are contagious, thrive in unsanitary conditions, and often followed wars. In fact, Zinsser (1935) argued that these two diseases were critical factors in history as they determined the course of important battles by weakening armies and ending sieges. In fact, in many wars, more people died of these diseases than combat. And again, it was the effectiveness of sanitation rather than the strategic brilliance of military leaders that determined victory.

Influenza

While influenza is an annual occurrence, it is rarely lethal; that is why the 1918 influenza pandemic still baffles epidemiologists. To this day, no solid explanation exists as to why this strain of the disease was as deadly and as virulent as it was. But deadly and virulent it was, infecting 500 million people (nearly a third of the world's population) and killing anywhere between 25 million and 100 million (Crosby, 2005). One of the major risk groups was young adults, normally a population at least risk, although some of that death toll might be accounted by the fact that many men in this bracket were in close quarters due to the First World War.

Many public health practices evident in addressing the coronavirus pandemic were employed during the four waves of the influenza pandemic. Schools and entertainment venues were closed, large gatherings were cancelled, and masks were recommended. As with prior pandemics, people wanted to identify its origins. Germany was blamed initially but also fell victim to the flu, stalling an important offensive. Spain, in fact, was the country that ultimately became associated with the flu. This happened both for the fact that much information about the flu censored by the warring parties was available in neutral Spain, as well as the fact the Spanish King Alfonso XII had the disease and his experience and eventual recovery were well covered by the press. To this day, many people erroneously believe the flu had its origins in Spain because of these associations. As with cholera, there were positive effects as well. Public health systems were again mobilized and modernized, and the electron microscope proved its worth.

Prior pandemics caused widespread economic and social disruptions. Yet as difficult and disruptive as they were, they were also a source of innovation and change.

COVID-19: THE NEW DREAD DISEASE

Since it was first identified in Wuhan, China in 2019, the coronavirus, generally known as COVID-19 or SARS-CoV-2, has spread rapidly. As this book goes to press, there are almost 82 million cases worldwide and close to 2 million deaths (WHO, Dec. 31, 2020). The United States has a large share of these cases with over 19 million cases and over 340,000 deaths (CDC, Dec. 31, 2020). Even beyond the deaths, the coronavirus has created widespread social disruption as nations placed restrictions on travel and imposed quarantines. Businesses, schools, entertainment, and restaurants have closed, leading to significant job losses as well as increased isolation.

There is little doubt that one consequence of this pandemic will be a pandemic of complicated forms of grief. Such a pandemic of grief will not only be due to the numbers of people who have been infected and who have died but also to the very nature of this pandemic.

Though medical science has made great strides in identifying the coronavirus, there is still much that is unknown, generating both uncertainty and anxiety. Some people are likely to be asymptomatic carriers of the virus; others may have cold or flu symptoms. In other cases, the effects might be more severe, and in anywhere from two to five percent of the cases, the infected person will die. Another concern is that COVID-19 symptoms can suddenly increase in severity, so a patient may seem to be stable or even improving prior to rapid decline, and possibly death. Often the symptoms are ones associated with many other illnesses, including fever, cough, respiratory difficulties, diarrhea, aches, and fatigue, so that almost any symptom may lead to anxiety that one has been infected by the coronavirus. Moreover, there is little known yet about the long-term effects of the disease. For example, there is no assurance that testing positive for antibodies to the disease offers future immunity nor do we know whether the virus may, at least in some infected individuals, result in other health problems later in life.

This anxiety has been exacerbated by the disruption of routine that people have experienced during the collective quarantine and the phased reopening. Aside from those deemed essential workers, most individuals have had to work from home, and many have been furloughed from work or lost their jobs. Students have seen their schools closed and have had to adjust to online learning. Sports, films, and other forms of entertainment (aside from television) have been canceled or limited. Children's camps, sports, and other activities have been canceled or restricted. The effects of this imposed social isolation are not yet known but are likely to include increased rates of alcoholism, domestic abuse, depression, and anxiety (Lee & Crunk, 2020; Choi et al., 2020). All of these factors can complicate grief.

The COVID-19 pandemic is a significant traumatic event. By that, it is meant that the pandemic has challenged our assumptive world; we no longer see the world as safe, predictable, or benevolent (Janoff-Bulman, 1992). This reality adds another complicating layer to grief as the world now is experienced as more dangerous and unexpected than believed. Therefore, in addition to coping with the death of a loved one, grievers are dealing with the loss of the world as once experienced, leading to increased anxiety and depression. Certainly, complicated grief will likely be experienced by a variety of populations. Obviously, families, friends, and those in the intimate network of individuals who have died as a result of COVID-19 infection are highly at risk for complicated grief reactions. These reactions can include a variety of complications including anxiety and somatic distress, depression, and posttraumatic stress (Chew et al., 2020).

These complications are not surprising, as a death from COVID-19 has a number of significant risk factors. COVID-19 is a new disease, highly contagious, and rapidly spreading. In addition, deaths from COVID-19 are also relatively sudden and unpredictable. Most deaths occur in less than three weeks after onset of symptoms. Moreover, there can be deaths such as suicides, yet uncounted, due to the impact of the pandemic.

Other factors can also complicate grief. The disease often presents multiple symptoms that can easily be attributed to other illnesses, generating guilt that a diagnosis and medical assistance was not proffered earlier. In addition, the highly contagious nature of the disease may evoke a sense of guilt in other survivors. Persons may experience survivor guilt because one person died from COVID-19 while others survived. In some cases, there may be death causation guilt where a given individual blames himself or herself for infecting another who died of the disease. During this time, deaths will also occur that are not related to COVID-19; any death during the pandemic can create conditions and factors that exacerbate the grieving process and may put survivors at risk.

Moreover, during the pandemic, persons may be experiencing multiple losses. These losses include not only the deaths of others but may include other losses such as the loss of income, employment, and other opportunities. Because of these multiple losses, persons may be forced to relocate or make significant changes in their lifestyles. Both multiple losses and concurrent crises are factors that complicate grief (Worden, 2018).

Finally, travel restrictions, limitations on gatherings, and quarantines limit the efficacy of rituals. Research has clearly demonstrated that while meaningful funerals can facilitate the grieving process, problematic funerals can complicate grief (Doka, 1984, 2016). During the pandemic, funerals are often restricted in numbers and expressions of intimacy such as hugging are inhibited, possibly leading to less meaningful rituals that subsequently complicate grief.

Medical and mental health personnel also are at risk for significant grief reactions in handling the COVID-19 pandemic. Research has shown that the medical and mental health staff can be vicariously traumatized by and grieve the deaths of patients (Papadatou, 2000; Katz & Johnson, 2016). In this pandemic there are a variety of factors that make many deaths in this period especially problematic. Medical staff have often had to become more attached to patients as they try to fill the social and emotional void left by loved ones who are unable to visit due to restrictions. Because of the overwhelming demands on the healthcare system, clinicians may have had to make difficult choices about care or not been able to deliver care at the standard they have come to expect for themselves and their patients, in addition to coping with their own fears about becoming infected or bringing the disease to their family and loved ones.

People experiencing nondeath losses in the pandemic are also likely to have significant grief reactions. In the past few decades, there has been increased attention to the nondeath losses that can generate grief (Doka, 1989; 2002, 2016; Harris, 2011, 2020). Though people may respond to trauma in different ways and with varying levels of intensity, the loss of an assumptive world—including the unpredictability and inability to plan for the future with any degree of a certainty—is a universal loss created by the pandemic.

Other nondeath losses may be more tangible. Loss of opportunities for education and extracurricular activities may have happened because travel restrictions are in place, schools and gyms are closed, and athletic and academic events are cancelled. Others might have lost jobs and income. Even if someone has not experienced the death of a loved one due to COVID-19, most have experienced some sense of loss as a result of the pandemic.

Conclusion

In an earlier work, I described two types of dreaded diseases (see Doka, 1997). One of the types was disease that stigmatized infected individuals, and others were great pandemics such as influenza. Certainly, the COVID-19 pandemic has become one of these diseases. Even though the mortality rate is relatively low, the widespread morbidity, the economic and social disruption it has created, and the rapid spread of the disease have wreaked considerable havoc and fear.

One result is a likely pandemic of complicated grief. All of the factors previously mentioned—the emergence of a new, high infectious disease; the social isolation and economic disruption; the sudden nature of death; the sheer volume of deaths, including multiple deaths in a single family; and the traumatic loss of our assumptive world—complicate grief. The nature of the pandemic is likely to leave a host of psychological issues, including hypochondria, anxiety, and all the varied forms of complicated grief. Even a rapid vaccination process, while preventing new cases, may complicate the grief of those mourning the deceased. Issues of "if only" (i.e., "if only the vaccine had been available two months ago") may exacerbate the mourning process.

Where there is grief, though, there is the possibility of growth. Past pandemics have led to improvements in health care, particularly in public health. Perhaps this pandemic will lead to a greater understanding of how animal viruses are evolving, enabling them to infect humans. Perhaps it will open up the development of new procedures that can quickly identify, control, and even set procedures to limit opportunities for viruses to adapt. The isolation that many are experiencing may create new appreciation of family and community. Certainly, it has already changed the nature of commerce and given a significant boost to telemedicine and even remote forms of offering therapy as well as spiritual support.

That this pandemic will leave a mark is inevitable. We can only hope that the legacy will be more than a body count or broken bereaved survivors coping with complicated grief, but that we as clinicians and practitioners will continue to learn the best ways to help all of us grow and heal.

Kenneth J. Doka, PhD, MDiv, is Senior Bereavement Consultant to Hospice Foundation of America (HFA) and the recipient of the 2019 Lifetime Achievement Award from the Association of Death Education and Counseling (ADEC). A prolific author and editor, Dr. Doka serves as editor of HFA's Living with Grief® book series, its Journeys newsletter, and numerous other books and publications. Dr. Doka is a past president of ADEC; a former board member of the International Work Group on Death, Dying, and Bereavement; and an advisory board member to the Tragedy Assistance Program for Survivors (TAPS). He is the recipient of The International Work Group on Death, Dying, and Bereavement's prestigious Herman Feifel Award and ADEC's Award for Outstanding Contributions in the Field of Death Education. Dr. Doka is an ordained Lutheran minister and a licensed mental health counselor in the state of New York. This is Dr. Doka's 28th year of involvement with HFA's Living with Grief® program.

REFERENCES

Aries, P. (1987). *The hour of our death.* New York, NY: Knopf.

Calhoun, L., & Tedeschi, R. (Eds). (2006). *Handbook of posttraumatic growth: Research and practice.* Mahwah, NJ: Lawrence Erlbaum.

Centers for Disease Control and Prevention (CDC). (2020). CDC COVID data tracker (maps, charts, and data provided by the CDC). Retrieved Dec. 31, 2020 from https://covid.cdc.gov/covid-data-tracker/#cases_casesper100klast7days

Chew, Q., Wei, K., Vasoo, S., Chua, H., & Sim, K. (2020). Narrative synthesis of psychological coping responses towards emerging infectious disease outbreaks in the general population: Practical considerations for the COVID-19 pandemic. *Singapore Medical Journal, (prepublication)*. doi.org/10.11622/smedj.202046)

Choi, E., Hui, B., & Wan, E. (May 25, 2020). Depression and anxiety in Hong Kong during COVID-19. *International Journal of Environmental Research and Public Health, 17*(10): 3740.

Claster, J. (1982). *The medieval experience: 300-1400.* New York, NY: New York University Press.

Crosby, A. (2005). *America's forgotten pandemic: The influenza of 1918.* New York, NY: Cambridge University Press.

Doka, K. (1984). Expectation of death, participation in planning funeral rituals and grief adjustment. *OMEGA—Journal of Death and Dying, 15,* 119-130.

Doka, K. (Ed.). (1989). *Disenfranchised grief: Recognizing hidden sorrow.* Lexington, MA: Lexington Books.

Doka, K. (1997). *AIDS, fear, and society: Challenging the dreaded disease.* Washington, DC: Taylor & Francis.

Doka, K. (Ed.). (2002). *Disenfranchised grief: New directions, challenges, and strategies for practice.* Champaign, IL: Research Press.

Doka, K. (2016). *Grief is a journey: Finding your path through loss.* New York, NY: Atria Press.

Harris, D. (Ed.). (2011). *Counting our losses: Reflecting on change, loss and transition in everyday life.* New York, NY: Routledge.

Harris, D. (Ed.). (2020). *Non-death loss and grief: Context and clinical implications.* New York, NY: Routledge.

Hourani, A. (1991). *A history of the Arab peoples.* Cambridge, MA: Belknap Press.

Janoff-Bulman, R. (1992). *Shattered assumptions: Toward a new psychology of trauma.* New York, NY: The Free Press.

Katz, R., & Johnson, T. (2016). *When professionals weep: Emotional and counter-transference responses in palliative and end-of-life care.* New York, NY: Routledge.

Lee, S. A., & Crunk, E. A. (August 6, 2020). Fear and psychopathology during the COVID-19 crisis: Neuroticism, hypochondriasis, reassurance-seeking, and coronaphobia as fear factors. *OMEGA—Journal of Death and Dying.*

Marks, G., & Beatty, W. (1976). *Epidemics.* New York, NY: Charles Scribner & Sons.

McNeill, W. (1976). *Plagues and people.* Garden City, NY: Anchor Books.

Papadatou, D. (2000). A proposed model of health professionals grieving process. *OMEGA—Journal of Death and Dying, 41,* 59-77.

Weber, M., & Kalberg, S. (2013). *The Protestant ethic and the spirit of capitalism.* London, UK: Routledge.

Worden, J. W. (2018). *Grief counseling and grief therapy: A handbook for the mental health practitioner (5th Ed).* New York, NY: Springer.

World Health Organization (WHO). (2020). WHO coronavirus disease (COVID-19) dashboard. Retrieved December 31, 2020 from https://covid19.who.int/

Zinsser, H. (1935). *Rats, lice and history.* Richmond, UK: Prelude Books Ltd.

CHAPTER 2

The Impact of COVID-19 on Black America

Paul C. Rosenblatt and Beverly R. Wallace

Authors' Note: In this chapter we use both the terms *Black Americans* and *African Americans* in part because some of the literature we cite uses one term and some the other. National statistics on racial differences typically use *Black* as a category, but in discussing culture and family history it makes sense to differentiate Black people who differ considerably in cultural and family background. And of course, the labels in this chapter are used because the chapter focuses on Black Americans/African Americans, but what term or terms any particular person uses in self-description (if any) should be respected.

DISPROPORTIONATE EFFECT OF COVID-19 ON BLACK AMERICANS

The death rate in the United States from COVID-19 is far higher among Black Americans than white Americans. According to the Centers for Disease Control and Prevention (CDC) (2020), the death rate for Black Americans is 2.8 times greater than for white Americans. Even when adjusted for age differences in racial groups, this death rate disparity remains virtually the same at 2.7 times greater (American Public Media, 2020).

Systemic Racism and Racial Disparity in Death Rates

Black Americans and their situations are diverse, but key to understanding the disproportionately higher death rate from COVID-19 for Black Americans in comparison to white Americans is the acknowledgment of systemic racism (Strickland et al., 2020). While there are many historic and economic realities regarding this issue, what follows is a brief and selective summary of those realities that may contribute to the higher Black American death rate from COVID-19.

Because of discrimination in education, hiring, and residential segregation, Black Americans are more likely than white Americans to have low-paid jobs that require high contact with others, making social distancing difficult and exposure to COVID-19 more likely. Think, for example, of what have during the pandemic been deemed as "essential workers"—a term that includes store clerks, workers in nursing homes and other care facilities, fast food workers, preschool teachers and day care workers, and transit system workers. Jobs like these do not allow working from home, and many of them may not provide adequate personal protective equipment (PPE). These jobs are also likely to provide either a small amount of paid sick leave or none at all, so Black Americans as well as others in these jobs may be reluctant to take time off from work if they feel ill, which can lead to their illness becoming more serious before they seek medical attention as well as to an increase in the potential spread of COVID-19. These same jobs are less likely to provide adequate health insurance, or any health insurance at all. That reality is part of why Black Americans are more likely to have preexisting health problems (Barrett, 2009), whether or not they are low income.

In addition, some preexisting conditions arise from or are made worse by the stress on Black Americans of living in a racist society (e.g., Simons et al., in press). Many of these preexisting conditions are in part due to what is often called environmental racism. Black Americans are relatively likely to live and work where there are more toxic chemicals, carcinogens, and particulates in the air, in the soil, in the drinking water, in locally grown food, and on the surfaces people touch (Berkovitz, 2020). A case can be made that preexisting conditions also arise from the ways that systemic racism has made it harder for people to afford and gain access to healthy foods and to move to safer environments. Of course, preexisting medical conditions (including diabetes, asthma, heart disease, obesity, lung disease, hypertension, and kidney disease) make it more likely that Black Americans will die from COVID-19 if infected.

Racial disparities in health care in the United States have been documented in thousands of studies (see Imhoff, 2020, for a recent review). These disparities contribute directly to the causes of the higher death rate from COVID-19 among Black Americans (Louis-Jean et al., in press). People living in predominantly Black American communities, many of which struggle with poverty and high unemployment, have less access to health care in general and to affordable or accessible COVID-19 testing. If they need to be hospitalized due to their illness, they are relatively likely to go to a hospital that primarily serves Black Americans; these hospitals statistically have lower quality care due to low budgets, disproportionately fewer critical care physicians, and a comparative shortage of supplies and equipment for treating COVID-19 (Louis-Jean et al., in press). With medical discrimination and healthcare disparities in the United States (Rosenblatt & Wallace, 2005a, pp. 10-14), if a very sick Black American goes to a hospital that treats both Black and white patients, and the hospital is short of intensive care beds, ventilators, or medications for treating COVID-19, the triage process may well make it less likely that Black patients will have access to those resources than white patients (Elbaum, 2020). For example, Elbaum asserts that health care is often rationed on the basis of an assessment of "years remaining." As many older African Americans may have more chronic diseases (due to earlier mentioned health disparities), they are likely to fare poorly in the triage process compared to white persons of the same age.

Wealth disparity is another factor. Even when Black families are not low income, the disparity in wealth adds a challenge in the ability to meet the financial needs necessary to sustain a family. One reason for this disparity is that, as a result of past and current discrimination in the housing and employment sectors, Black Americans have much less savings and assets in comparison to white Americans (Ross, 2020, summarizing data from the U.S. Federal Reserve). That reality makes it harder to leave a job where one is in danger from COVID-19, less likely to afford the loss of income from staying home if ill, and less likely that one can self-finance medical care. This income and wealth inequality also may mean that Black Americans are more likely to live in crowded housing and crowded communities, which makes isolation and quarantine difficult when someone is infected. And as is the case with hospitals, many Black Americans in eldercare facilities are likely to be in facilities that are less resourced and may have higher patient-to-staff ratios that make it harder to prevent the spread of COVID-19.

Another aspect of the COVID-19 pandemic in the United States that may disproportionately add challenges for Black Americans is the shift to much of health care being delivered by electronic means, often known as telehealth or telemedicine. Telemedicine can protect patients and medical providers from infection and disease, but telemedicine only works when the patient has the appropriate electronic devices and access to the internet. A recent study of Black and Latino patients in New York City (Jercich, 2020) concluded that "disparities in digital access, digital literacy, and telehealth awareness, as well as issues of cost and coverage, and mistrust of digital appointments where physical examinations, labs and vitals cannot be taken are all potential barriers to telehealth." This "digital divide" may put Black Americans at a comparative disadvantage that leads to higher mortality rates from COVID-19, especially because much COVID-19 screening and medical advice, particularly in the early stages of the illness, is disproportionately done via telemedicine in response to the pandemic.

Another significant and ongoing concern is the issue of Black Americans' trust, or mistrust, of the medical system (Aten, 2020; Barrett, 2009; Powell et al., 2019). Many older Black Americans well recall the Tuskegee syphilis study, conducted without the patients' informed consent, that documented the varied stages of the disease in Black men for 40 years, well after an effective treatment was available. This historical reality led to similar suspicions in the onset of HIV/AIDS and a general, generational mistrust of the healthcare system by many Black Americans. Distrust can translate into reluctance to seek medical testing and medical care, even during a pandemic, and that may contribute to the higher mortality rate of Black Americans.

From another perspective on issues of trust, it is a common belief in some African American communities, as evidenced on social media and other anecdotal experience, that the federal government's inadequate addressing of COVID-19 during 2020 arose in part from key government leaders recognizing that the death rate from COVID-19 was higher among Black Americans and hoping that by limiting the federal response to the disease the disease would kill disproportionately more Black Americans. That suspicion of genocidal motivation may seem absurd to some readers of this chapter, but it is a suspicion that fits the long history of medical discrimination in the United States.

With Black Americans more likely to be without health insurance or adequate health insurance, having poorer access on average to COVID-19 care and treatment, being more likely to have serious illnesses other than COVID-19, and being reluctant because of trust issues to seek medical care, many Black Americans may have died from COVID-19 but were not counted in official statistics because they were not tested for COVID-19 or could be said to have died from something other than COVID-19. That means that the ratio of Black American to white American deaths from COVID-19 may be even higher than the figures from the CDC and American Public Media cited at the beginning of this chapter.

Systemic Racism and What is Grieved

Taken together, the factors discussed above help to explain the much higher mortality rate from COVID-19 of Black Americans. These factors are also part of what Black Americans who are dealing with a family or community death may be grieving. Thus, it may not be just the tragic death of the person but also the reality of systemic racism which led to work and living conditions that made exposure to COVID-19 more likely; the lack of sufficient access to medical care; home and community limitations to social distancing; preexisting conditions the deceased might have had; the impact of environmental toxins; and all the other health-undermining factors linked to racism. Consistent with that, in an interview study about African American grief that we conducted, roughly half the interviewees felt that racism was a contributing cause of the death of the person whom they were discussing (Rosenblatt & Wallace, 2005a).

A case can be made that, in Black communities, living with systemic racism makes family and community connection precious in part because those connections help to deal with the stress, frustrations, dangers, and limitations imposed by a racist society. This reality means that the restrictions required by COVID-19 of social distancing, including the closing of face-to-face church services and other religious events; the closing down of social meeting places; the movement of schools to distance learning; the inability to visit family members in nursing homes and other care facilities; the potential loss of childcare support from older family members in order to protect their health; the cutting back or elimination of extracurricular activities, including sports, for young people; and the reduction or elimination of family and friend get-togethers, and the hugging and other physical connection that may go on at those, constitute a loss of communal support in a difficult time in an already burdened community. All of these losses add to what is grieved by Black Americans (Aten, 2020).

Some Black Americans may experience "suffocated grief" (Bordere, 2020) in a white context. Here expressions of grief are not only unacknowledged but likely to be misinterpreted, discouraged, and even punished. For example, a Black child experiencing the typical cognitive or behavioral manifestations of grief is more likely to be perceived as oppositional or learning disabled rather than bereaved. When someone important in a Black American's life dies of COVID-19, the frustration and feelings of loss arising from all these other challenges and losses may compound the tears, sadness, anger, and other expressions of grief. If a bereaved person talks about the life of the deceased, part of what they may talk about is frustration over how the deceased person struggled with racism and therefore was limited in opportunities, or with pride about how that person overcame these challenges (Rosenblatt & Wallace, 2005a, pp. 19-27; 2005b). For many Black Americans, the importance of family, friends, and community is paramount because the institutions of the larger society often cannot be trusted to be free of danger, frustration, humiliation, prejudice, and discrimination. Black Americans may be grieving the special ways that the person who died was a support and resource in facing those ongoing challenges and burdens.

GRIEF SUPPORT FOR BLACK AMERICANS

Given the current realities, what can be said to someone providing grief counseling, grief therapy, or grief support for a Black American grieving one or more deaths from COVID-19? In our past research, we found that not many African Americans seek grief counseling or therapy (Rosenblatt & Wallace, 2005a, pp. 148-152); however, the few who had sought therapy in our study reported feeling helped by it. Some interviewees in this study were only willing to see an African American therapist, whom they felt would be much more understanding of African American life experiences, feelings, losses, and family situations. This finding suggests that, for many grieving Black Americans, the help they will receive will ordinarily be from family or community members, not professional counselors or therapists.

Can white bereavement professionals provide adequate support to Black Americans? The immediate answer is "of course," but the research suggests that white counselors may not "get" all that is going on with a Black person who is grieving and that there may be an understandable level of mistrust. White bereavement professionals must strive to be knowledgeable about Black life and racism and be open to learning and accepting client realities. One way for white bereavement professionals to start is by assessing and examining their own possible personal attitudes, prejudices, and even obliviousness to the issues brought about by systemic racism and how these realities may impact their work. Being real, empathic, caring, and attuned to where the other is must always be the first goal of bereavement support and professional help.

The limitations on gatherings resulting from COVID-19 make it difficult or impossible to have the kinds of well-attended visitations, wakes, burials, and post-burial meals that are commonly part of caring support in Black American communities following a death. Condolence calls are also health risks. Even hugging someone who is grieving, or having a brief, caring, face-to-face conversation with someone who is grieving, risks their health and one's own. Research has shown that these expressions of honoring the dead, of community support, and of witnessing are important to many African Americans (Rosenblatt & Wallace, 2005a, pp. 29-42; cf. Barrett, 2009). These types of gatherings are places where people can feel supported in expressing their grief, even if they weep, wail, or pass out; they are venues for exchanging stories and making meaning of the person's life; and they even offer opportunities for amusement, songs, and laughter that can be important in dealing with the loss.

The consequence of COVID-19 restrictions means that, in addition to the loss of loved ones, there is a genuine loss associated with the inability to have these shared and supportive rituals and informal social supports. Black Americans may also be grieving the ways that lockdowns and prudent social distancing keep them from the support of a Black religious congregation and Black clergy. Black families may also miss the full range of services of a Black funeral director, though they may still rely on a Black funeral director to see that the deceased receives a proper burial. Older family members may also grieve that the absence or curtailment of these rituals and supports means that children in the family do not learn about those community death rituals and how to behave in them.

With the COVID-19 shutdown, one kind of support that counselors can provide is to help bereaved people, their close family, friends, and all who want to support them to connect online. Some Black Americans, because of the issues around the "digital divide" addressed above, particularly older people and those who have less access to the internet, may need some instructions and loaned equipment so they can make connections with others for virtual visitations, virtual wakes, virtual funerals, or virtual condolence calls.

CONCLUSION

To end racial disparities in death rates from COVID-19 and other disease, society would need to commit to changing policies that encourage inequities in health care, the economy, the workplace, and housing. It would also be crucial that a host of other absent supports would also be present, including high-quality eldercare, affordable childcare, and paid sick leave, as well as access to online communication tools that would enable as many people as possible to work from home, attend school from home, and engage in telemedicine consultations.

In our thinking, the key to creating a society without racial disparities in death rates from COVID-19 would be the creation of a society in which racism in all its forms was identified, criticized, and made to be seen as not only unfair, cruel, and even murderous but also not good for anyone. For example, no one benefits when Black Americans are infected at a relatively high level with COVID-19, if for no other reason than that increases the likelihood of infection for all. Unfortunately, the historic and ongoing tragedy of systemic racism has led to the additional cruelty of a death rate from COVID-19 for Black Americans that is much higher than for white Americans. The historic and ongoing experience with racism may hurt even more Black Americans who may understandably mistrust the vaccines that hold the promise to protect them and others from death or lingering effects of the disease. Rebuilding that trust is essential to the medical and spiritual health of the nation.

Paul C. Rosenblatt, PhD, is Emeritus Professor of Family Social Science at the University of Minnesota. He has published 14 books, including African American Grief *(with Beverly R. Wallace);* The Impact of Racism on African-American Families; Shared Obliviousness in Family Systems; Parent Grief: Narratives of Loss and Relationship; Help Your Marriage Survive the Death of a Child; Multiracial Couples *(with Terri A. Karis and Richard Powell); and* Grief and Mourning in Cross-Cultural Perspective *(with R. Patricia Walsh and Douglas A. Jackson). His current projects include a study of when and how couples who are courting through love letters have written about death, dying, and bereavement. He also is writing short stories to try to illuminate aspects of bereavement that might be missed or are hard to study in bereavement research.*

Beverly R. Wallace, MDiv, PhD, *is currently the associate professor of Congregation and Community Care at Luther Seminary in St. Paul, MN. Dr. Wallace has authored several articles and book chapters including* Narratives of Grieving African Americans About Racism in the Lives of Deceased Family Members; A Womanist Legacy of Trauma, Grief, and Loss: Reframing the Notion of the Strong Black Woman Icon; Hush No More: Constructing an African American Lutheran Womanist Ethic; *and is the co-author (with Paul Rosenblatt) of* African American Grief. *Her current research agenda includes understanding community trauma and end-of-life decisions among older African Americans. She is also in the process in writing her second book,* African American Grief – Revisited.

REFERENCES

American Public Media (December 19, 2020). *The color of coronavirus: Covid-19 deaths by race and ethnicity in the United States.* https://www.apmresearchlab.org/covid/deaths-by-race

Aten, J. D. (October 2, 2020). Consequences of COVID-19 in African American communities: An interview with Dr. Rodlescia Sneed on her research in Flint, Michigan. *Psychology Today.* https://www.psychologytoday.com/intl/blog/hope-resilience/202010/consequences-covid-19-in-african-american-communities

The Atlantic. (October 15, 2020). *Covid Racial Data Tracker.* https://covidtracking.com/race

Barrett, R. (2009). Sociocultural considerations: African Americans, grief, and loss. In K. J. Doka & A. S. Tucci (Eds.), *Living with grief: Diversity and end-of-life care* (pp. 79-91). Washington, DC: Hospice Foundation of America.

Berkovitz, C. (May 19, 2020). Environmental racism has left Black communities especially vulnerable to COVID-19. *The Century Foundation.* Retrieved from https://tcf.org/content/commentary/environmental-racism-left-black-communities-especially-vulnerable-covid-19/

Bordere, T. C. (2020). Suffocated grief, resilience, and survival among African American families. In M. H. Jacobsen & A. Petersen (Eds.), *Exploring grief: Toward a sociology of sorrow* (pp. 188-204). Philadelphia, PA: Routledge.

Centers for Disease Control and Prevention (November 30, 2020). COVID-19 Hospitalization and Death by Race/Ethnicity. Retrieved Dec. 19 from https://www.cdc.gov/coronavirus/2019-ncov/covid-data/investigations-discovery/hospitalization-death-by-race-ethnicity.html

Elbaum, A. (2020). Black lives in a pandemic: Implications of systemic injustice for end-of-life care. *Hastings Center Report, 50*(3): 58-60. doi: 10.1002/hast.1135

Imhoff, J. (June 3, 2020). Health inequality actually is a 'Black and white issue," research says. Retrieved from *Michigan Health News*, December 15, 2020. https://healthblog.uofmhealth.org/lifestyle/health-inequality-actually-a-black-and-white-issue-research-says

Jercich, K. (September 1, 2020). Study: NYC Black and Latino patients less likely than white patients to use telehealth during pandemic. *HeathcareIT News*. https://www.healthcareitnews.com/news/study-nyc-black-latino-patients-less-likely-white-patients-use-telehealth-during-pandemic

Louis-Jean, J., Cenat, K., Njoku, C. V., Angelo, J., & Sanon, D. (in press). Corona virus (Covid-19) and racial disparities: A perspective analysis. *Journal of Racial and Ethnic Health Disparities*. doi: 10.1007/s40615-020-00879-4

Powell, W., Richmond, J., Mohottige, D., Yen, I., Joslyn, A., & Corbie-Smith, G. (2019). Medical mistrust, racism, and delays in preventive health screening among African-American men. *Behavioral Medicine, 45*(2), 102-117.

Rosenblatt, P. C., & Wallace, B. R. (2005a). *African American grief.* Philadelphia, PA: Routledge.

Rosenblatt, P. C., & Wallace, B. R. (2005b). Narratives of grieving African Americans about racism in the lives of deceased family members. *Death Studies, 29*, 217-235. doi: 10.1080/07481180590916353

Ross, J. (June 12, 2020). The racial wealth gap in America: Asset types held by race. *Visual Capitalist.* www.visualcapitalist.com/racial-wealth-gap/

Simons, R. L., Lei, M. K., Klopack, E., Zhang, Y., Gibbons, F. X., & Beach, S. R. H. (in press). Racial discrimination, inflammation, and chronic illness among African American women at midlife: Support for the weathering perspective. *Journal of Racial and Ethnic Health Disparities.* doi: 10.1007/s40615-020-00786-8

Strickland, O. L., Powell-Young, Y., Reyes-Miranda, C., Alzaghari, O., & Giger, J. N. (2020). African Americans have a higher propensity for death from COVID-19: Rationale and causation. *Journal of the Black Nurses Association, 31*(1): 1-12.

CHAPTER 3

Challenges to Hospice and Palliative Medicine in the COVID-19 Pandemic

Leah McDonald

Anticipating and managing the grief that patients and families will experience related to chronic illness, the dying process, and loss of a loved one are key aspects of practice in hospice and palliative medicine (HPM). COVID-19 has presented unprecedented challenges to HPM in providing this support in the context of how grief is approached during "normal" practice times.

CHALLENGES SPECIFIC TO DEATH AND GRIEF DURING COVID-19: WHAT'S DIFFERENT?

COVID-19 is a disease with a high morbidity and mortality rate. Nineteen percent of patients with COVID-19 will develop severe or critical disease and 5-10% will require intensive care (Wu & McGoogan, 2020). Mortality rates are between 3% and 6% (Baud et al., 2020). Original prognostic data is based on cases in China; however, the data has been constantly evolving over the course of this pandemic, leading to a fluid understanding of how the disease progresses and prognosis for individual patients (Murthy et al., 2020). This uncertainty of clinical outcome leads patients and families to feel scared, unsupported, and in the dark about what will happen to them once they are diagnosed with COVID-19. If the person diagnosed with COVID-19 dies, this dissatisfaction with understanding of the clinical outcome, as well as some of the challenges faced by the type of support that can be offered during the illness and dying process, can impact the griever and even lead to complicated grief (Miyajima et al., 2014).

The Conventional Approach to Grief in Hospice and Palliative Medicine

While sudden deaths can occur in the context of hospice and palliative medicine, understanding how grief is generally supported in those settings is important in order to contrast how the realities of COVID-19 are impacting the grieving process and the role that HPM clinicians can play in providing support. In a typical palliative care setting, patients receive a diagnosis of a serious illness early in the disease process. While there is grief associated with the diagnosis and prognosis, these emotions can be approached in a gentle and slow manner over multiple office visits in the outpatient setting or in the hospital during an inpatient admission. Clinicians can facilitate open communication and a celebration of life, and help families to complete "unfinished business." Anticipatory grief can be experienced both by the person with a life-limiting illness and diagnosis as well as by family members who are anticipating life without their loved one. Anticipatory grief refers to emotions related to the expectation of death and the dying process.

As a patient approaches death, clinicians in the hospice setting support a patient and their loved ones prior to and after the person's death. This role includes providing guidance surrounding what to expect during the dying process, ensuring the patient has a peaceful dying process whenever possible, and educating families that their loved one is not suffering. All of these important factors can help assure that families feel that their loved one's last moments were meaningful (Tenzek & Depner, 2017). After a patient's death, hospice and bereavement professionals, including social workers and grief counselors, can provide support as well as assess who may be at risk for complicated grief. The concept of complicated grief is based in attachment theory, which emphasizes the idea of abandonment after death (Kissane & Zaider, 2015). In the hospital setting, three elements predicted the development of complicated grief: dissatisfaction with the explanation to the family about the patient's expected outcome, unreasonable cost of care, and the family's perception that the deceased person had not achieved a sense of completion about his or her life (Miyajima et al., 2014).

A Good Death

The concept of "a good death" is of particular importance in this context as it relates to how people may grieve after the death of a loved one. Some of the key factors identified as important in a good death may include symptom management, meeting hopes and expectations, strong social relationships and support, spiritual and existential beliefs, psychological and cognitive symptoms, and economic demands (Emanuel & Emanuel, 1998). Patients see dying in their sleep quickly, peacefully, and pain-free as ideal (Payne et al., 1996). Families have views on what makes a good death, too. A thorough understanding of what to expect for the patient's clinical outcome and feeling the patient reached a sense of "completion" are both key (Miyajima et al., 2014); if the griever has perceived that a good death was achieved, the bereavement process is more well-adapted.

THE REALITIES OF COVID-19 AND THE IMPACT ON FAMILIES AND HOSPICE AND PALLIATIVE MEDICINE PROVIDERS

Rapidity of Symptoms and Deterioration

COVID-19 is a respiratory illness that can progress quickly, leading to clinical deterioration from talking and communicating to requiring intubation within hours (Murthy et al., 2020). Some have likened death during the COVID-19 pandemic to a sudden traumatic event. Family members of those who die from a sudden traumatic event are at risk for complicated grief (Clements et al., 2004). The rapid change in symptoms and often quick deterioration can lead to a sense of "unfinished business," such as not having the opportunity to say goodbye, share expressions of love and gratitude, or resolve past differences; losing some or all components of a perceived "good death" as described above can be one factor that puts families at risk for developing complicated grief (Miyajima et al., 2014).

Contagious Disease

Deaths during pandemics differ from those typically managed in the HPM field. While loved ones and patients go through the dying process and bereavement period for a patient with cancer, there is little fear of "catching" the dying person's disease. During this pandemic, there is the additional heightened anxiety of people in close proximity to an infectious patient. People may also blame or stigmatize those diagnosed with a contagious disease (Cohn, 2012). This anxiety and potential stigma can heighten feelings of guilt as well as other reactions among the bereaved.

Personal Protective Equipment (PPE)

Guidance and hospital policies on required PPE has changed throughout the pandemic. For the care of a COVID-19 patient, the checklist often includes an N95 mask, a face shield, a gown, and gloves. This combination of equipment provides an effective barrier between the person wearing the equipment and the contagious virus. Yet it also creates a physical barrier between providers and patients, which creates significant problems in verbal communication. Even basic physical shows of support, such as a gentle touch on the shoulder or hand, are more awkward. The presence of PPE often affects a patient's ability to hear the actual words being communicated (Hampton et al., 2020). Verbal communication from providers requires the use of short sentences and exaggerated emotional responses.

Isolation

Soon after the beginning of the COVID-19 pandemic, visitor restrictions were put in place in nursing homes, hospitals, and hospice settings. Policies have differed across institutions and have changed over time at individual settings. These restrictions were put in place to meet the obligation of hospitals to ensure safety of staff, patients, and visitors by implementing social distancing (Virani et al., 2020) and were enforced with public health interests in mind. Variation in rules across institutions were determined by local factors (local infection rates, PPE supplies, size of the hospital) as well as national guidance (Centers for Disease Control and Prevention [CDC] and public health guidelines).

Unfortunately, there are unintended consequences to the enforcement of visitor restrictions. HPM providers treat many patients who reside in congregate settings such as rehabilitation centers and nursing homes. While residents who live in these settings may not be acutely ill, they often experience a decline in functional status while living there. During COVID-19, family and friends do not witness this decline firsthand due to visitor restrictions. When a patient requires transfer to the hospital for an acute illness, family has likely not seen them for weeks to months and have a different image in their minds of their loved one's health and functional status.

This discrepancy is a particular challenge to HPM providers. A major technique used in goals of care conversations is information sharing, which requires determining what a family member knows about their loved one's recent functional level and medical diagnoses. If a family has not seen their loved one in some time, and the already overworked staff has not had the ability to share their day-to-day progress, it is a challenge to catch up with the patient's decline. It may seem to the family that this change in status is "out of the blue," making it difficult to make medical decisions in keeping with medical reality.

The acute care setting has seen similar restrictions. A few versions of visitor policies included allowance of visitors during strict visitor hours; visitors allowed if needed to provide ideal care (for dementia patients or young children); or visitors allowed only at end-of-life situations. Some hospitals restricted visitors without exceptions, including for dying patients (Valley et al., 2020). Enforcement of this restriction has fallen on frontline providers, which challenges rapport building since it can be seen as having a lack of empathy for the family and loved ones' desire and need to be with the person who is ill (Virani et al., 2020). The grief response can be more intense when family feels that they and their loved one were not treated with empathy.

Lack of Resources

The resources of an HPM physician include medications for symptom management, an interdisciplinary team, and communication skills. Many of these tools that allow physicians to facilitate a "good death" have been limited by the realities of the COVID-19 pandemic.

Regarding symptom management, close assessments are important to ensure symptoms are well managed. To protect physicians and nurses during the pandemic, time in a patient's room is limited. This limited interaction may lead to untreated symptoms of pain, dyspnea, or anxiety. Additionally, some resources, such as nebulized medications and non-invasive positive pressure ventilation (BiPAP or CPAP) are considered at high risk of aerosolizing virus particles and continue to be restricted in most hospital settings (Hendin et al., 2020).

The interdisciplinary team is at the center of the HPM model. The contribution of chaplains and social workers helps facilitate quality end-of-life care. During COVID-19, many hospitals have restricted the number of staff allowed to enter patients' rooms. Chaplains and social workers are required to do virtual visits from outside the room. This added barrier to a type of care that relies heavily on nonverbal communication presents a challenge to quality care, as care providers cannot offer what is often called "a ministry of presence."

Communication skills are a key element of HPM practice. One example of a model for communication skills is the SPIKES protocol for delivering bad news. The steps include: **Setting** up a discussion; assessing the patient's **perception** of the situation; obtaining the patient's **invitation** to share information; sharing **knowledge** with the patient; addressing **emotion**; and developing a **strategy** and summary (Baile et al., 2000). During COVID-19, setting up such a discussion is a challenge. Visitor restrictions mean having family meetings by phone, which requires coordinating multiple people and multiple phone numbers. Assessing understanding is also difficult given time restrictions with these critically ill patients. Addressing emotion is a skill that relies heavily on nonverbal signs. A touch on the shoulder or providing a tissue when someone demonstrates strong emotions is impossible to do by telemedicine, and even in person is not ideal when wearing a full PPE suit.

ADAPTATIONS AND RESPONSE TO THE PANDEMIC: HOW HAVE HOSPICE AND PALLIATIVE MEDICINE PRACTICES SHIFTED?

Role of Technology

There is no question that across medicine and the public arena, technology has played a huge role in the adaptation to COVID-19. Given visitor restrictions, most hospitals encourage visits by family and loved ones to happen by phone or videoconferencing (Valley et al., 2020). This change in procedure reduces the number of visitors in the hospital and allows for improved social distancing implementation. Use of telemedicine in communication around the end-of-life is challenging, but providers have been able to adapt and implement meaningful discussion tools. Allowing family to see bedside caregivers demonstrating human touch with patients during video calls, educating families about what to anticipate during the call, and incorporating spiritual care and social workers into video visits all improve the experience for families at the end of life (Ritchey et al., 2020).

Innovative Interactions

Since standard interaction with patients and families is significantly limited by PPE and other safeguards, providers need to be creative with how to bring compassion and a personal touch to interactions. One innovation seen commonly in hospitals includes putting the providers' names on the front of their face shields or a photo of themselves on their gowns (Nicholls & Saada, 2020). This small gesture brings an element of humanity to patient care.

Providers have created new ways to ensure proper symptom management for patients. Limits on interactions between infected patients and care providers have led to the development of "palliative order sets," which are groups of patient orders that can be placed in the hospital electronic medical record for all patients suffering from symptoms related to COVID-19. They include all the proper parameters to manage symptoms at the end of life, such as morphine for air hunger and lorazepam for anxiety (Etkind et al., 2020). Additionally, nursing staff have created innovative ways to safely administer medications, including using long tubing to allow the monitoring and adjustment of medications to occur from outside the room (Shah et al., 2020). This technique ensures the patient gets needed medications while keeping nursing staff safe.

Fields across medicine have realized the emotional scope of this pandemic and have made changes to practice. Many hospitals have incorporated HPM into the emergency department (ED) with the knowledge that the overwhelming volume of patients with life-threatening COVID-19 symptoms did not allow for meaningful goals-of-care conversations. Given that most patients who present to the ED do not have advance directives (Yadav et al., 2017), when a patient presents seriously ill from symptoms of COVID-19, it often falls on the frontline providers to have these conversations with patients and families. HPM providers have been able to implement meaningful advanced care planning using evolving COVID-19 prognostic tools and preparing families for anticipated decline in clinical status and likely death (Wallace et al., 2020). Embedding HPM specialists in the ED leads to more patients forgoing mechanical ventilation and CPR in cases where meaningful recovery is likely not possible (Lee et al., 2020).

Shared Experience

Challenging times such as pandemics, wars, and economic depressions can be seen as communal experiences. A unifying mentality can balance the isolation contributing to anxiety and grief. This bonding experience is one that HPM providers can use to their advantage in patient care. Allowing patients and families to know they are not alone in their experiences can give the patient and their intimate network a sense of comradery. This approach needs to be taken with care to not minimalize or objectify each individual's experience. Additionally, although this is a comfort to those whose loved ones died of COVID-19, it has the potential to make those who died of other diagnoses during the time of COVID-19 feel as though their deaths are not as significant, so HPM providers supporting the bereaved also need to be conscious of this reality when providing care.

"Shared trauma" between patient and provider is occurring at this time. HPM providers are going through the same pandemic as their patients; some may have lost family and friends to the disease or have similar fears about contracting the virus through work or other exposure. Acknowledgement of this shared environment can allow for a deeper bond between patient and provider (Tosone et al., 2012). During this pandemic, it is common to hear a family member telling the provider to "take care of yourself."

Memory Making

Grief can often be tempered by lasting memories of a loved one. For the patient, techniques such as dignity therapy, which allows a person to create a document that is a "testament of their life," has been proven to reduce depression and anxiety in the seriously ill population (Martinez et al., 2017). For loved ones, this memento provides a sense of closure. During COVID-19, the ability to write letters and share photos still exists even if there is not the opportunity for a more formal life review process, and actually may be of even more importance (Death with Dignity, 2020). Social workers and chaplains have adapted the use of iPads and phone calls to facilitate this process with the assistance of nurses and other healthcare providers. For example, a patient may be able to dictate a letter to a social worker by phone and have the nurse bring the letter into the patient's room to sign.

GRIEF SUPPORT: HOW HAS THE BEREAVEMENT PROCESS CHANGED?

Professionals

Visitor restrictions alone place a huge burden on healthcare professionals (Virani et al., 2020). Without family at the bedside, comfort and support falls onto professionals. Providers have been required to shoulder multiple emotional burdens in addressing the challenges of this pandemic. Engaging in the dying process leads to long-term grief for health professionals if not processed in a healthy manner. Additionally, providers across specialties rely on family presence to facilitate meaningful goals-of-care conversations. In this restrictive setting, providers can feel they have not completed their job to the best of their ability, leading to emotional distress (Valley et al., 2020).

Staff debriefing is a long-used tool for sharing the burden of caring for sick and dying patients (Harrison & Wu, 2017). Formal versions of case discussions exist, such as Balint groups, which enhance the doctor-patient relationship through exploration of difficulties encountered during challenging patient cases (Knowlton & Katz, 2016). Residency training programs and hospitals also implement debriefing sessions after challenging cases. These debriefings are of particular importance during COVID-19 where witnessing multiple deaths and suffering can lead to provider burnout (Hendin et al., 2020).

Families

Hospice provides significant support to patients and families at the end of life and during the grieving period. Unfortunately, the process of enrolling in hospice has become more burdensome for patients with COVID-19, as well as for non-COVID-19 patients. Hospice staff are often limited from performing in-person evaluations in nursing home, hospitals, and at home due to limited PPE or facility rules and regulations. Completing enrollment forms has been a challenge given that even when hospice staff can evaluate the patient, the responsible family is not at the bedside. Additionally, there are limited beds available at inpatient hospices, which are easily overwhelmed when there are high numbers of critically ill symptomatic patients in the service area.

One of the specific benefits of enrolling in hospice is the availability of bereavement support. This benefit involves social work, chaplaincy, and access to grief counselors, both in the form of individual counseling sessions and group sessions. Telemedicine and internet resources have been able to reach grieving individuals, changing the form in which support occurs.

One particular challenge for grieving families has been the lack of in-person death rituals, including funerals and burials. HPM providers should provide supportive care related to this limitation, including allowing for voiced disappointments and creating new "rituals" such as virtual ceremonies, delayed memorial services, and creation of memory making prior to death (Death with Dignity, 2020).

DISPARITIES EXPERIENCED DURING COVID-19

Historical Context

Disparities in health care have long existed in communities of color. Access to care, treatments provided, and health outcomes are uniformly different. For patients of color in palliative care, there are higher rates of mortality, shorter life expectancy, greater difficulty with access to healthcare services, higher rates of chronic disease, lower rates of cancer screening, and lower rates of hospice usage. People of color are less likely to receive the right amount of emotional support and symptom management, are more likely to have an advanced stage of cancer at the time of diagnosis, and are less likely to have an advance directive or to have had discussions about end-of-life goals (Johnson, 2013).

Disparities During the Pandemic

In models tracking case and death rates during COVID-19, of the 49 out of 56 states and territories reporting race/ethnicity data, 47 of the 49 states experienced healthcare disparities in communities of color as of August 2020 (COVID Tracking Project, 2020). Looking at a cohort of patients in Louisiana, where Blacks made up 31% of the population in the area, 76.6% of the hospitalizations and 70.6% of the deaths were of Black patients (Price-Haywood et al., 2020).

Using New York as a model, it is evident that coronavirus affects those in poor neighborhoods at higher rates (van Dorn et al., 2020). There are multiple contributors to the disparities in care for people of color. Availability of testing differs based on location and ethnicity of the inhabitants (Lieberman-Cribbin et al., 2020). In addition, the underlying health vulnerability of patients of color, who suffer higher rates of diabetes, asthma, and hypertension, puts patients at higher risk for complications from COVID-19 (Pareek et al., 2020). People of color are also facing increased exposure to the disease. Higher rates of employment in "essential services" or the necessity of continuing work due to financial needs, especially among undocumented people who are not eligible for unemployment benefits, place this population at higher risk. There are also concerns over group cohabitation that occur among more impoverished patients leading to disease "hot spots" (van Dorn et al., 2020). For those patients of color unfortunate enough to contract COVID-19, they receive overall poorer quality of care compared to white patients, leading to worse outcomes. The large role of telemedicine during COVID-19 has the potential to heighten disparities, given that many in communities of color and other underserved communities have less access to computers, less technologic literacy, and less access to the internet (Velasquez & Mehrotra, 2020).

Effects on Grief

Higher rates of death in communities of color means increased risk for complicated grief. Additionally, knowledge among these communities regarding their increased risk of contracting and dying from COVID-19 leads to heightened anxiety (Purtle, 2020). Losses in this population lead to lower educational achievements, more marital problems, and poor mental and physical health, further exacerbating existing social discrepancies (Verdery et al., 2020). The fact that those who contract COVID-19 do not receive similar treatment leads to significant discontent surrounding the death of a loved one and contributes to complicated grief (Eligon & Burch, 2020; Miyajima et al., 2014).

"Acute on chronic" grief is a concept prevalent in particular groups, such as with Black Americans. The disparities experienced during this pandemic are only a reminder of the injustices that have existed for years in America. While this acknowledgement can lead to feelings of despair, it also has the potential to lead to continued bonds between those with similar backgrounds, as well as motivation for civil and political change (Manning, 2020).

CONCLUSION

Support throughout the grieving process is an important aspect of care provided by HPM physicians. COVID-19 has proved a challenge to many of the techniques that providers use to approach grief, as people are grieving differently now, and the tools used to combat complicated grief are limited. Adaptations such as use of technology, innovative interactions, evoking a shared experience model, and memory making are all adjustments being used by HPM providers. This pandemic presents constantly evolving changes to the practice of medicine. The field of HPM will continue to adapt to the needs of patients and their families, with supportive care and eliciting patients' goals remaining at the core of the practice ethic.

Leah McDonald, MD, is a practicing emergency medicine physician as well as a hospice and palliative medicine physician. She received her medical degree from Tufts University School of Medicine in Boston, MA. She completed an Emergency Medicine residency at New York University/Bellevue Hospital and a fellowship in Hospice and Palliative Medicine at Brown University/Hope Health Hospice in Providence, RI. She was the recipient of the Izeman Award, recognizing humanistic treatment in the geriatric population. She has clinical interests in improving primary palliative care services especially among emergency physicians and integrating palliative and hospice services within the healthcare system in more streamlined systems. She practiced in the palliative medicine, hospice, and emergency department settings during the COVID-19 pandemic.

REFERENCES

Baile, W. F., Buckman, R., Lenzi, R., Glober, G., Beale, E. A., & Kudelka, A. P. (2000). SPIKES – A six-step protocol for delivering bad news: Application to the patient with cancer. *Oncologist, 5,* 302-311.

Baud, D., Qi, X., Nielsen-Saines, K., Musso, D., Pomar, L., & Favre, G. (2020). Real estimates of mortality following COVID-19 infection. *Lancet Infectious Disease, 3099*(20), 30195.

Clements, P. T., DeRanieri, J. T., Vigil, G .J. & Benasutti, K. M. (2004). Life after death: Grief therapy after the sudden traumatic death of a family member. *Perspectives in Psychiatric Care, 40,* 149-154.

Cohn, S. K. (2012). Pandemics: Waves of disease, waves of hate from the Plague to Athens to AIDS. *Historical Journal, 85*(230), 535-555.

Death with Dignity. (2020). Dying – and grieving – during a pandemic [blog post]. Retrieved from https://www.deathwithdignity.org/news/2020/05/dying-grieving-during-pandemic

Eligon, J., & Burch, A. D. S. (2020, May 10). Questions of bias in COVID-19 treatment add to the mourning for Black families. *New York Times.* Retrieved from http://www.nytimes.com

Emanuel, E. J., & Emanuel, L. L. (1998). The promise of a good death. *Lancet, 351,* 21-29.

Etkind, S. N., Bone, A. E., Lovell, N., Cripps, R. L., Harding, R., Higginson, I. J., & Sleeman, K. E. (2020). The role and response of palliative care and hospice services in epidemics and pandemics: A rapid review to inform practice during the COVID-19 pandemic. *Journal of Pain and Symptom Management, 60*(1), e31-e40.

Goldman, J., & Xyrichis, A. (2020). Interprofessional working during the COVID-19 pandemic: Sociological insights. *Journal of Interprofessional Care,* online ahead of print. doi: 10.1080/13561820.2020.1806220

Hampton, T., Crunkhorn, R., Lowe, N., Bhat, J., Hogg, E., Afifi, W.,… Sharma, S. (2020). The negative impact of wearing personal protective equipment on communication during coronavirus disease 2019. *The Journal of Laryngology and Otology, 134*(7), 577-581.

Harrison, R., & Wu, A. (2017). Critical incident stress debriefing after adverse patient safety events. *American Journal of Managed Care, 23*(5), 310-312.

Hendin, A., La Riviere, C., Williscroft, D., O'Connor, E., Hughes, J., & Fischer, L. (2020). End-of-life care in the emergency department for the patient imminently dying of a highly transmissible acute respiratory infection (such as COVID-19). *Canadian Journal of Emergency Medicine, 22*(4), 414-417.

Johnson, K. S. (2013). Racial and ethnic disparities in palliative care. *Journal of Palliative Medicine, 16*(11), 1329-1334.

Kissane, D. W. & Zaider, T. I. (2015). Bereavement. In N. I. Cherry, M. T. Fallon, S. Kaasa, R. K. Portenoy, & D. C. Currow (Eds.). *Oxford Textbook of Palliative Medicine* (5th ed.), pp. 1110-1122. New York, NY: Oxford University Press.

Knowlton, K., & Katz, R. S. (2016). Balint groups to address countertransference and burnout in palliative and end-of-life care. In Katz, R., & Johnson, T. (Eds.). *When professionals weep: Emotional and countertransference responses in end-of-life care.* New York, NY: Routledge.

Lee, J., Abrukin, L., & Flores, S. (2020). Early intervention of palliative care in the emergency department during the COVID-19 pandemic. *JAMA Internal Medicine, 180*(9), 1252-1254.

Liberman-Cribbin, W., Tuminello, S., Flores, R. M., & Taioli, E. (2020). Disparities in COVID-19 testing and positivity in New York. *American Journal of Preventive Medicine, 59*(3), 326-332.

Manning, K. D (2020). When grief and crises intersect: Perspectives of a Black physician in the time of two pandemics. *Journal of Hospital Medicine, 15*(9), 566-569.

Martinez, M., Arantzamendi, M., Belar, A., Carraso, J. M., Carvajal, A., Rullan, M., & Centeno, C. (2017). "Dignity Therapy," a promising intervention in palliative care: A comprehensive systematic literature review. *Palliative Medicine, 31*(6), 492-509.

Miyajima, K., Fujisawa, D., Yoshimura, K., Ito, M., Nakajima, S., Shirahase, J.,...Miyashita, M. (2014). Association between quality of end-of-life care and possible complicated grief among bereaved family members. *Journal of Palliative Medicine, 17,* 1025-1031.

Murthy, S., Gomersall, C. D., & Fowler, R. A. (2020). Care for critically ill patients with COVID-19. *JAMA, 323*(15), 1499-1500.

Nicholls, I. F., & Saada, L. (2020). Rapid response: Communication, confusion, and COVID-19: The challenges of wearing PPE on a geriatrics ward during the COVID-19 pandemic. Re: Patient perspective: Gordon Sturmey and Matt Wiltshire. *BMJ, 369,* m1814.

Pareek, M., Bangash, M. N., Pan, D., Sze, S., Minhas, J. S., Hanif, W., & Khunti, K. (2020). Ethnicity and COVID-19: An urgent public health research priority. *Lancet, 395*(10234), 1421-1242.

Payne, S. A., Langely-Evans, A., & Hiller, R. (1996). Perceptions of a good death: A comparative study of the views of hospice staff and patients. *Palliative Medicine, 10,* 307-312.

Price-Haywood, E. G., Burton, J., Fort, D., & Seoane, L. (2020). Hospitalization and mortality among Black patients and white patients with Covid-19. *New England Journal of Medicine, 382,* 2534-2543.

Purtle, J. (2020). COVID-19 and mental health equity in the United States. *Social Psychiatry and Psychiatric Epidemiology, 55*(8), 969-971.

Racial Data Dashboard. The COVID Tracking Project at The Atlantic. Retrieved from https://covidtracking.com

Ritchey, K. C., Foy, A., McArdel, E., & Gruenewald, D. A. (2020). Reinventing palliative care delivery in the era of COVID-19: How telemedicine can support end of life care. *American Journal of Hospice and Palliative Medicine, 37*(11): 992-997.

Shah, A. G., Taduran, C., Friedman, S., Sarosky, K., Jones, M., Victory-Stewart, M.,…Yimen, M. (2020). Relocating IV pumps for critically ill isolated coronavirus disease 2019 patients from bedside to outside the patient room. *Critical Care Explorations, 2*(8), e0168.

Tenzek, K. E., & Depner, R. (2017). Still searching: A meta-synthesis of a good death from the bereaved family member perspective. *Behavioral Sciences, 7*(2), 25.

Tosone, C., Nuttman-Shwartz, O., & Stephens, T. (2012). Shared trauma: When the professional is personal. *Clinical Social Work Journal, 40,* 231-239.

Valley, T. S., Schutz, A., Nagle, M. T., Miles, L. J., Lipman, K., Ketcham, S. W.,…Hauschildt, K. (2020). Changes to visitation policies and communication practices in Michigan Intensive Care Units during the COVID-19 pandemic. *American Journal of Respiratory and Critical Care Medicine, 202*(6), 883-885.

van Dorn, A., Cooney, R. E., & Sabin, M. L. (2020). COVID-19 exacerbating inequalities in the US. *Lancet, 395*(10232), 1243-1244.

Velasquez, D., & Mehrotra, A. (2020). Ensuring the growth of telehealth during COVID-19 does not exacerbate disparities in care. *Health Affairs Blog.* Retrieved from https://www.healthaffairs.org/do/10.1377/hblog20200505.591306/full

Verdery, A. M., Smith-Greenaway, E., Margolis, R., & Daw, J. (2020). Tracking the reach of COVID-19 kin loss with a bereavement multiplier applied to the United States. *Proceedings of the National Academy of Sciences Jul 2020, 117*(30), 17695-17701.

Virani, A. K, Puls, H. T., Mitsos R., Longstaff, H., Goldman R. D., & Lantos, J. D. (2020). Benefits and risks of visitor restrictions for hospitalized children during the COVID pandemic. *Pediatrics, 146*(2): e2020000786.

Wallace, C. L., Wladkowski, S. P., Gibson, A., & White, P. (2020). Grief during the COVID-19 pandemic: Considerations for palliative care providers. *Journal of Pain and Symptom Management, 60*(1), e70-e76.

Wu, Z., & McGoogan, J. M. (2020). Characteristics of and important lessons from the coronavirus disease 2019 (COVID-19) outbreak in China: Summary of a report of 72,314 cases from the Chinese Center for Disease Control and Prevention. *JAMA, 323*(13), 1239-1242.

Yadav, K. N., Gabler, N. B., Coney, E, Kent, S., Kim, J., Herbst, N.,... Courtright, K. R. (2017). Approximately one in three US adults completes any type of advance directive for end-of-Life care. *Health Affairs, 36*(7): 1244-1251.

CHAPTER 4

Voices
COVID-19 Reflections: Maintaining Patient-Centered Care

Mary McDonald

As I think back to the early days of the COVID-19 pandemic, I am amused by some of the assumptions that I had in preparation for the first possible surge. I've been a hospice medical director since 2004, for most of my career. Who better to be ready for an influx of dying patients than a hospice physician? I know death. I understand the dying process. Each death is unique but there are some core principles that I remind myself of often to help stay on course as I advocate for patients and family.

I decided to use these core principles as the foundation for our pandemic response in hopes that this would achieve the best possible outcomes for our community. These core principles are:

- Most people want to be in the comfort of their home when they die.
- Most people want to be surrounded by their loved ones when they die.
- Most people want their suffering minimized when they are dying through good symptom management.

Many months later, hundreds of thousands of Americans have died of COVID-19 and at publication time, the death rate shows no sign of slowing down. I have painfully learned that the typical death scenarios that I had encountered are anything but typical during a pandemic. The strain on our medical system has made respecting the three core principles not only difficult to achieve for my COVID-19 patients, but also challenging to achieve for the non-COVID-19 patients, who are caught in the crossfire of this pandemic battle.

Most patients wish to be in the comfort of their own home when they die; the COVID-19 pandemic has made reaching this end-of-life goal very challenging. COVID-19 tends to infect members of households together and this leads to the absence of a caregiver in the home, as everyone is sick with the virus. Those who aren't sick are, understandably, wary of exposing themselves to this dangerous illness by accepting a dying patient infected with the virus back into their home. Under normal circumstances, some families with the means to do so can hire private-duty caregivers to help with the caregiving duties. This model changes completely if families find that the home health staffing agencies in their area are not agreeing to enter a home with COVID-19 infection due to personal protective equipment limitations, concerns about maintaining a healthy workforce, and not carrying the infection to other homes. Getting COVID-19 infected patients who have been hospitalized back home has been particularly difficult, so care teams have made conscientious efforts to help patients avoid hospitalization altogether. Area nursing homes were encouraged to call palliative medicine providers prior to sending patients to the emergency department (ED) to discuss goals of care, advance directives, treatment decisions, and whether an ED visit even made sense. In addition:

- ED providers were authorized to prescribe a comfort pack for patients to take home, with hospice follow-up the next day in their home and access to the hospice triage line immediately.
- Patients who are hospice eligible cannot stay in the hospital, as those beds are needed for other patients. We doubled occupancy in our residential hospice house by making all rooms semiprivate and took in hospice patients who couldn't return home. This option is not as good as getting them home, but it does provide a more comfortable environment.

I don't believe I really understood how tremendously therapeutic our loved ones can be until I was faced with the lonely pandemic death. Managing end-of-life symptoms for patients who are not allowed to be in the presence of loved ones, being held and talked to and comforted, is tremendously challenging. The patients I have treated have been more dyspneic, more anxious, and have had more pain. A dying person's circle of people can bring great comfort and being kept from them can bring incredible sorrow and distress. The grief that family members who are kept from the bedside as their family members die is the most profound, raw grief I've ever encountered.

Hospitals in our area have very limited visiting policies, and some allow no visitors. An assigned visitor or two can stay with patients at our residential hospice house but a maximum of two visitors is allowed in order to limit exposure of our staff. I have witnessed a mother have to choose which two of her three adult children could be with her when she died; situations like this cause everyone, including me, pain. In our practice, we have tried to be as creative as possible to allow the death that people want.

One patient declined tracheotomy for chronic ventilation. She wished to be extubated and allowed to die, but not in the intensive care unit, in part because the hospital was on lockdown to all visitors at the time. She wanted to go home and be surrounded by her family and friends. We transferred her home on a ventilator and I extubated her in her living room; the hospice nurse and I then managed her symptoms. Her friends and family filed in one after another to say goodbye and she died within a few hours.

Another patient was dying, and his wife could not fathom compassionate extubation without her by his side, but the hospital would not allow any visitors at that time. We transferred him with the ventilator to our residential hospice house and extubated him there. His wife stayed by his side for the next few days until he died. We had not previously done extubations in the home or residential hospice setting.

At the residential hospice house, we promoted outside visitation on the deck whenever possible, with basic masking protocols and 6-foot distance maintained. Hospice nurses were able to offer another layer of telecommunication between nursing home patients and their families. Nurses were encouraged to videocall families during each nursing home patient visit to offer opportunity for engagement.

Highlighting the need to balance diagnostic and curative interventions with effective symptom management for all patients is the battle cry of all hospice and palliative medicine providers. This is challenging under normal circumstances, but exponentially more so during a pandemic surge. Hospitals are crowded with very sick people. Patients are being sent home from the ED and the hospital because they are less sick than the others and hospital beds are at a premium. Under these circumstances, symptom management may seem like a luxury to some practitioners as they are truly just trying to keep their heads above water in managing the increased patient census and meeting the immediate medical needs of these very sick patients.

In preparation for the first COVID-19 surge, our hospice team pointed out that if patients came to the ED because they felt miserable and were sent home without symptom management, they would be back. We anticipated a group of patients who would choose to return to their home with aggressive symptom management instead of being admitted to the hospital; these were anticipated to be patients who were older and had already indicated on their advance directives that they did not want to be intubated. They did not, however, want to suffer without any care at all. These were the patients that we targeted for discharge home with a comfort pack and follow up with the hospice team in their home or nursing home environment.

Medicines can help alleviate many symptoms, but it is the powerful effect of the interdisciplinary team that really makes hospice special. I've long recognized the psychospiritual benefit of sharing the caregiving role with the rest of the team. Currently, our social workers, music therapist, chaplains, and veteran liaisons are performing most of their tasks remotely via video conference with patients. The patients are best served by their actual presence, and it has been an ongoing challenge to meet the expectations that we have set for ourselves as a hospice team. Some hospice team members who are passionate about the work that they do are finding themselves dissatisfied with the limitations on what they CAN do while adhering to pandemic restrictions. It can be demoralizing and add to the burden for professional caregivers.

I am still finding myself in a position of having more questions than answers about hospice care during a pandemic. My goal as the medical director has been to keep the focus on the three core principles focusing on comfort, family, and symptom management, and to secure the safety of the hospice team from this deadly infection. We are still in the trenches of the second COVID-19 surge as I am writing this, so I may lack the vantage point to assess our true performance yet. When the day comes for true retrospection, I am forever grateful that I will be doing so as a member of a fantastic hospice team.

Mary McDonald, MD, *is the Medical Director of Frederick Health Hospice in Frederick, MD, and completed all of her medical training at The University of Kansas School of Medicine. After completing medical school there, she completed a family medicine residency and then a geriatrics fellowship. She is board certified in family medicine with added qualifications in geriatrics and hospice/palliative medicine. She has been a hospice medical director for most of the last 16 years in Kansas and then Washington, DC, and Maryland.*

CHAPTER 5

Death and Dying in America's Nursing Homes: The Impact of COVID-19

Elaine Healy

Making rounds in a nursing home just north of New York City on a grim morning in early March 2020, I saw a man being pushed towards me in his wheelchair by a well-dressed woman visitor. Almost completely paralyzed from the neck down, Jay had recently been admitted for physical therapy following emergency surgery on his fractured spine. Devotedly, the woman leaned down and repositioned his hands on the armrests, caressing his hair as he beamed at her; I lingered nearby, unwilling to leave the aura of their love. I had been feeling uneasy; after nearly 40 years of practice in nursing homes and 20 years as a facility medical director, I sensed that something ominous was about to happen. A few weeks earlier I had heard that a new virus capable of killing human beings was spreading rapidly around the globe. Initially, I hadn't been too concerned; other pandemic viral infections had occurred in recent years and none had affected my world. However, I had just learned that the very first outbreak of the virus in America was occurring in, of all places, a nursing home. The casualties at Life Care Center in Kirkland, Washington, were escalating and I couldn't get the images of the sick and dead being carried out on stretchers out of my mind.

"You two are so sweet!" I said. Jay proudly responded that he and Sharon had been married for 50 years, having fallen in love while competing as partners in the U.S. National Roller Skating Championship in the late 1970s. "You're kidding!" I exclaimed; prompted to cue up YouTube on my laptop, I was treated to a grainy black-and-white video of them skating in perfect synchrony to garbled waltz music, arms about each other's waist, heads touching.

Four days later I stood guard in the facility's lobby, turning Sharon away as she frantically tried to enter the building. New York's first COVID-19 patient was from New Rochelle, the very city in which my facility was located. As contact tracing revealed skyrocketing local cases, I realized that the events of Kirkland could very well play out in my own facility. To lower the risk of introducing the virus, I convinced the administration to enact a nonvisitation policy, days before the governor mandated it. "How long is this going to last?" Sharon cried out in anguish. "He needs me!" Considering the typical 2- to 4-week course of a seasonal influenza outbreak, I hastened to reassure her: "Don't worry; it should be over soon. We'll take good care of him."

COVID-19 in Nursing Homes: A Perfect Storm

When COVID-19 slammed into the New York metropolitan region, images of overcrowded emergency departments and exhausted healthcare workers tending to the critically ill attested to an overwhelmed hospital system. Untold at the time was the experience playing out in the area's nursing homes. As the press and health authorities focused on the struggling hospitals, the virus swiftly decimated the region's long-term care population. Eventually, the presence of refrigerated trucks functioning as overflow morgues outside of nursing homes and the anguished demands for information by family members could not be ignored. Over time it was revealed that the region's nursing homes were being consumed by outbreaks fueled by shortages of personal protective equipment (PPE), testing materials and, many believe, a controversial mandate to accept COVID-19 patients from hospitals (Miltimore, 2020).

Tragically, by the end of November 2020, the virus had claimed the lives of over 100,000 of America's nursing home residents, accounting for a shocking 40% of the nation's then 250,000 pandemic fatalities; in 14 states, at least half of all COVID-19 deaths were linked to nursing homes (Chidambaram et al., 2020). No longer able to ascribe the situation to being unprepared, facilities in state after state continue to experience fatal outbreaks despite having implemented the infection prevention and control strategies mandated by the Centers for Disease Control and Prevention (CDC) and local health authorities (Connole, 2020). In early March 2020, active screening of residents and healthcare personnel for fever and respiratory symptoms became standard operating procedure, communal dining and group activities were severely restricted, and volunteer and nonessential healthcare services were suspended. In a stunningly draconian measure, all family visitation, with the exception of known end-of-life situations, had been virtually eliminated (Centers for Medicare & Medicaid Services, 2020). Staff members and as many residents as possible continue to be masked at all times; procedures for isolation and management of cases have been disseminated and implemented. Most facilities have designated specific areas for those sick with the virus; these COVID-Only Units, often created at the expense of relocating residents, are required to have separate staff. In New York, mandates that facilities must test their staff on an ongoing basis were enacted in June 2020, and state health surveyors have conducted multiple, unannounced facility inspections at the homes to ensure compliance with these measures. Yet, even with all of these procedures and protocols, "Our worst fears have come true as COVID has run rampant across the country; nursing homes have become powerless to keep it from entering our buildings" (Parkinson, 2020).

"Like Fire Through Dry Grass"

The presence of multiple chronic health conditions, coupled with a sluggish immune response and diminished physical reserves, renders older adults particularly susceptible to COVID-19; compared to their counterparts in the community, institutionalized frail older adults have an even significantly higher risk both of contracting and dying from illness (DeSmet et al., 2020). Historically congregating in communal dining and recreational areas and often sharing semiprivate bed and bathrooms, a resident may have multiple, close interactions with dozens of different people over the course of a day. As many as six residents may be assigned to the same nursing assistant, a caregiver who performs such intimate tasks as dressing, feeding, bathing, and personal hygiene.

While the role of mandates to accept COVID-19 patients for admission is fiercely debated, asymptomatic but infected staff members are considered to be the primary means by which COVID-19 is introduced into nursing homes (Gandhi et al., 2020). Once inside a facility, transmission from resident to resident swiftly occurs. In a press conference in April 2020, New York Governor Andrew Cuomo described the virus' impact on nursing homes as reacting "like fire through dry grass." Given these realities, some consider that the "single greatest error of America's response to the pandemic in nursing homes...was the failure to provide early and vast access to virus testing for residents and staff. Without testing, nursing home staff focused on isolating residents who showed symptoms of the virus, while asymptomatic residents and staff continued to spread the virus throughout the facilities" (Eaton, 2020).

Infected nursing home residents exhibit a wide array of COVID-19 disease manifestations (Tang et al., 2020). Most develop fever, dry cough, and weakness for a period lasting 7 to 14 days before eventually recovering; however, at the same point in the illness, some who appear to be improving can rapidly deteriorate and succumb. Still others experience an illness of lesser intensity, but one that lingers for many weeks and results in a prolonged convalescence. Most shocking are those who suddenly collapse, deteriorate, and die over the course of only a few hours; with barely enough time to be notified, families are stunned when they learn that their loved one has become critically ill or suddenly perished.

In the throes of a nursing home outbreak, physicians must simultaneously attend to the ill, access limited information available about treatment options and outcomes, apprise family members of their loved one's condition, and assist patients and families in medical decision making. The presence of advanced directives outlining wishes about aggressive treatments and hospitalizations can render this process less burdensome; when these are not available or the family has not had these conversations with their loved one, families become severely stressed. "These were not discussions about death that followed a long illness, giving both patient and family a chance to say goodbye and accept the inevitable. The sudden, shocking nature of COVID forced families to address a fatal illness without warning and without the ability to provide the comfort of their presence" (Powell & Chuang, 2020). Although not quantified, it is likely many families chose hospitalization rather than risk incurring the guilt of thinking that they had not done everything possible. Residents that remained on site were given oxygen, fluids and, when necessary, morphine to ease respiratory distress. Ironically, some hospices, particularly smaller organizations without the ability to maintain separate COVID-19 teams, were not able to enroll patients who were positive for COVID-19. Despite the fact that compassionate visits were allowed when a resident was recognized as being at the end of life, these visits were not always possible to facilitate due to the rapidity of the resident's decline, especially if the family was not nearby. Nursing home staff heroically held phones to the ears of the dying as distraught family members frantically said their goodbyes. Tragically, "many patients have died of COVID-19 in isolation while disconnected from family and friends, and their loved ones have also experienced forced separation and an inability to share important feelings, provide comfort, and find closure" (Abbott et al., 2020).

Information from early nursing home COVID-19 outbreaks revealed that 60% of residents may have become ill simultaneously and mortality rates rose to 27% (McMichael et al., 2020). In addition to residents, multiple staff members may become sickened during a nursing home outbreak; although exact data is lacking, facilities at which a significant number of frontline caregivers get sick simultaneously, or those that lost key clinical leaders such as the director of nursing or an attending physician, likely incurred increased resident casualties. After several weeks, an outbreak gradually abates, and the survivors begin their recovery. Information pertaining to the long-term outcomes is currently mostly anecdotal; while many eventually regain their previous level of health, prolonged cognitive deficits have been observed (Healy, 2020). Nursing homes that experienced heavy mortalities, however, may never return to life as it was before.

Battle Scarred and Beleaguered

Fearful of contracting and then transmitting the illness among their charges and families, traumatized frontline nursing home caregivers witnessed death on a scale matched only on the battlefield or in a mass casualty event. Unlike their counterparts in the hospital, however, nursing home staff often had long-standing, close relationships with those who died, causing an emotional toll that is still largely unacknowledged. In addition, the heroic efforts of nursing home staff during the pandemic have not been lauded as have those of their counterparts in the acute care setting; instead, they are perceived as having brought the disease into the nursing homes, making the facilities in which they labor unsanitary (Williams, 2020). To date, over 1,250 long-term care staff have died from COVID-19 (CMS, 2020), the majority of whom were certified nursing assistants, a shocking statistic that is barely acknowledged (Ellis & Hicken, 2020). In 2018, the last year for which data is available, the Bureau of Labor Statistics reported a total of 5,147 "fatal work injuries" across all industries (Blanchard,

2020); however, it is doubtful that 2020 COVID-19-related deaths of nursing home staff will be counted in future statistics since those deaths are not the result of accidents. Arguably, working as a certified nursing assistant in a nursing home is now one of the most hazardous occupations in America; if such a rate of death occurred in any other sector there would be a huge outcry and demands for reform. Instead, barely a whisper is heard as these devoted professionals quietly continue to show up to work and care for their residents.

Through a Glass and Darkly: COVID-19's Collateral Casualties

Within days of the first case in New Rochelle, our formerly welcoming lobby was turned into a quasimilitary screening and PPE distribution station. Staff members were rendered nearly unidentifiable as face masks, eye shields, head coverings, and surgical scrubs became the garb of necessity. Residents were confined to their rooms; families and visitors vanished. The auditorium, once the scene of concerts, bingo games, and birthday celebrations, was transformed into a COVID-19 testing center. Dining areas and lounges, formerly scenes of fellowship and conversation, fell silent. Entering the Therapeutic Recreation suite in search of some decorations, I beheld a woman silhouetted against a window, shoulders heaving, head in her hands; I backed out quickly, the sound of the door closing concealed by her weeping.

Jay escaped COVID-19 but became increasingly despondent as the days separated from his beloved Sharon turned into weeks and, ultimately, months. FaceTime, window visits, and phone calls could not raise his mood. Without his life's partner at his side to coach, cheer, cajole, and touch him, the "can-do" attitude which had sustained him through the first weeks following his accident faded and the bleak reality of his situation took over. He was permanently crippled and dependent on others; his aging wife would never be able to take him home. He would spend the rest of his life in a nursing home, perhaps forever separated from his family. He began to view himself as a burden to his loved ones and to think it would be better for all if he were gone.

Ultimately, Jay stopped taking in food and fluids so as to bring about his own demise, a process known as Voluntary Stopping of Eating and Drinking (VSED) (Compassion and Choices, 2020). Psychiatric assessment revealed that he was not experiencing a psychotic form of depression and that he fully understood the ramifications of his decision;

medications were initiated but did not change his mood. His devoted family protested that he was not a burden to them; his strong faith assured him, however, that a better life awaited him in the hereafter. Since he was not afflicted with COVID-19 he was able to access hospice care and, ironically, Sharon and his family were then allowed compassionate visits. After several weeks Jay died, not from COVID-19, but from a broken heart.

As we approach the first anniversary of the pandemic, it is becoming painfully clear that while not all nursing home residents have been directly infected by the virus, there is "another epidemic ravaging America's nursing homes—an outbreak of loneliness, depression, and atrophy fueled by the very lockdowns that were imposed to protect them from the coronavirus" (Healy et al., 2020). With the exception of end-of-life situations, virtually all nursing home visitation has been suspended, a paradoxical violation of the federal mandate to "permit immediate access to a resident, subject to the resident's right to deny or withdraw consent at any time, by immediate family or other relatives of the resident" (U.S. Code, 2006). Currently, a patchwork of state and federal guidelines tie visitation to the results of now mandatory, ongoing staff testing; many states, including New York, have imposed stricter thresholds than those of the CDC. At a minimum, visitation must be suspended for at least two weeks whenever a staff member tests positive, regardless of whether or not that individual goes on to develop symptoms; this is also the case whenever a resident has a positive test result. A recurring cycle of scheduled-then-cancelled visitation sessions has ensued, repeatedly dashing the hopes of families and residents.

Once a vital part of the nursing home community, visiting families provided countless benefits to both residents and staff. Rooms decorated with personal memorabilia, polished fingernails, occasional home-cooked meals, trips to the facility café or garden and, of course, loving kisses, hugs, and caresses are priceless contributors to a resident's quality of life. For those suffering from dementia, families serve as cognitive and emotional anchors, familiar faces who can trigger fading memories and engender a sense of safety and well-being. Families are often the first to note the subtle changes in their loved one's behavior that may signal a developing acute illness; their ability to alert the staff can result in early, potentially life-saving interventions.

Despite earnest efforts by staff, window and virtual visits are a poor substitute for in-person ones. Residents with dementia frequently cannot understand that they should be interacting with the person whose image is on the screen and, to the dismay of the family, focus their attention on the staff member present instead. Many residents struggle to see through the glare of the glass separating them from their loved ones and, despite amplification, to understand what is being said from the other side. Family members who may have travelled long distances for these brief encounters often leave frustrated and distressed. Sadly, however, even in-person visits can be unsatisfactory. Visitors must wear masks which not only conceal facial expressions but also muffle voices; many nursing home residents are hard of hearing and rely on both volume and lip reading to understand what is being said. One resident with dementia failed to process that his masked wife, finally allowed compassionate visits, was actually present next to him after only having had virtual visits for many months.

Nearly a year of absence of in-person family visitation has resulted in ominous trends among residents including increased confusion, apathy, and weight loss. The percentage of long-term residents experiencing depressive symptoms in New York State has doubled over the last 12 months, while nationwide it has increased by nearly 50% (CMS, 2020). It is unknown but likely that mortalities are linked to this reality, as it was in Jay's case. Family members, patient and understanding at first, have commenced to protest (Healy et al., 2020); however, with surging cases and cold weather arriving in many regions, there is no immediate relief in sight.

NURSING HOMES AND PALLIATIVE CARE IN THE COVID-19 ERA: THE TIME IS NOW

Although required by federal and state licensing agencies to maximize the health and longevity of their residents, death and dying has always been a familiar part of nursing homes; prior to COVID-19, about one in three deaths in the United States occurred in such facilities (Temkin-Greener et al., 2013). The majority of permanent residents are significantly disabled, suffering from multiple chronic illnesses as well as incurable diseases such as dementia and advanced cancer; those receiving short-term, postacute care are often similarly afflicted. Hospitalizations are frequently detrimental and burdensome for frail older adults and can cause serious medical complications such as delirium, falls, and bedsores (Creditor, 1993). Those hospitalized at the end of life are often subjected to intensive care unit (ICU) transfers, intubation, and CPR, interventions which, even in the pre-COVID era, have notoriously poor outcomes in this population (Tresch et al., 1993).

As a result of the hospice and palliative care movement of the last 20 years, many facilities have established formal palliative care programs; in 2016, 80.7% of nursing homes offered hospice services to their residents (HHS, 2019). Nursing homes are equipped with experienced interdisciplinary teams (IDTs) comprised of nurses, physicians, social workers, dieticians, and recreation and rehabilitation staff; facility residents are assessed on a regularly scheduled and as-needed basis. With the participation of residents and families, IDTs collaboratively devise and implement an individualized plan of care, adjusting it over time as the situation changes. When the resident's condition has progressed to the point that it is appropriate for the plan of care to pivot to an exclusively comfort-oriented approach, the management of chronic conditions and attempts to reverse acute events such as infections becomes secondary and the minimization of pain and suffering becomes paramount. At this point (pre-pandemic), an end-of-life care plan would be enacted, with the target goal of a peaceful death, ideally with the presence of loved ones at the death bed.

A core component of all palliative care programs is advance care planning (ACP), a process by which individuals specify the extent they wish to receive medical treatment in the event that they lose capacity to make healthcare decisions, as well as to designate an alternate decision-maker to make choices consistent with their wishes when such loss of capacity occurs. For those wishing to forgo medically futile interventions at the end of life, such choices are operationalized in the nursing home setting by way of physician orders against the institution of CPR; more compelling in the era of COVID-19, however, is the issue of future hospital transfers.

The suddenness of COVID-19 outbreaks in nursing homes and the disease's often rapidly fatal progression in this population have shown how crucial it is that facilities review and update each resident's advanced directives and specifically address the issue of hospitalization. Recently published data reveal that the mortality rate associated with intubation and mechanical ventilation of elderly COVID-19 patients is close to 100%, even higher than previously acknowledged (Shao et al., 2020);

since this has been one of the compelling reasons for hospital transfer in the past, residents and families must now be strongly advised as to its futility. In addition, monoclonal antibody therapy will imminently be available in nursing homes; as this is a promising treatment reserved for nonhospitalized elderly patients with COVID-19, there may well be a significant advantage to maintaining these residents in the facility.

A recently published study found that resuscitation and hospitalization preferences among nursing home residents changed after proactive, COVID-19-specific ACP conversations with their healthcare practitioners. The overall hospitalization rate was 1.47 times higher for nursing home residents who had ACPs that did not address hospitalization status compared to those that did, and 2 times higher for those without any ACP conversations at all (Ye et al., 2020). With nursing home COVID-19 cases continuing to climb, solid ACP discussions that address hospitalization preferences can spare families and residents the distress of having to make decisions during a medical crisis and perhaps even improve survival outcomes. Those patients who die despite the therapeutic efforts rendered in the facility will have a higher likelihood of dying among those that have long cared for them, including, ideally, their loved ones.

A New Year Brings Reason to Hope

As 2021 begins, the nation and world have cause to believe that the COVID-19 pandemic will soon be over, perhaps even within the year. Highly effective vaccines with few short-term side effects have been developed with astonishing rapidity and released by the Food and Drug Administration (FDA) under its Emergency Use Authorization process. As this book goes to press, these vaccines are in the process of being administered to those designated to be in the first phase of recipients. In acknowledgement of the toll of COVID-19 among nursing home residents and staff, both groups are included among the earliest to be vaccinated. Although not tested in the nursing home population, elderly patients were participants in the clinical vaccine trials; outcomes revealed that over 95% of vaccine recipients were protected against severe COVID-19 disease (CDC, 2020). If comparable results occur in the facility setting, it may be that significant outbreaks will no longer occur; in addition, courageous nursing home staff will receive the protection they deserve, and residents and their loved ones will finally be reunited.

As the holiday season approached, I could not stop thinking about Jay's wife. It would be her first Christmas without him; how could someone who had been so perfectly partnered since she was a young woman adapt to being alone in her old age? My sense of guilt, irrational as it was, troubled me. Haunted by the expression on her face when I stopped her from coming into the facility to see her husband, I felt that I had abandoned them, witnessing their final dance from a distance, gazing at him as he lay dying from the safety of the doorway. Would she allow me to share their story? Would she forgive me?

After being contacted by Jay's devoted social worker, Sharon graciously accepted my call. Yes, she remembered me, and yes, she welcomed our conversation. She was sad, of course, but was slowly adjusting to life without him. She was particularly stricken when she contemplated the boxes of Christmas decorations which he had so carefully stored away just before their lives were shattered by his accident; they went unused this year, she explained. But overall, she was full of gratitude for their life together, the love that would never die, and, in particular, for those who cared for Jay in his last days. "Please, please, tell them I said 'thank you' for everything. They were wonderful. I know they did everything they could. We were blessed. Please, will you tell them?" As I choked back my tears, I replied "Yes , of course; I will tell everybody."

Elaine Healy, MD, FACP, CMD, *is the vice president of medical affairs and medical director at United Hebrew of New Rochelle, a multi-service healthcare organization that includes a 300-bed skilled nursing facility, two senior independent housing units, two assisted living facilities, and a robust home care program. She is board certified in Internal, Geriatric and Hospice and Palliative Medicine and is a certified medical director by the American Medical Directors Association. Dr. Healy is a clinical assistant professor of medicine at New York Medical College and has implemented programs in geriatric medical training and care at two community hospitals. Dr. Healy is currently the President-elect of the New York Medical Directors Association and is a member of the American Medical Directors Association's Ethics and Infection Control Committees. By virtue of her early experience with COVID-19 in nursing homes, she has taken a leadership role in the latter organization's educational and advocacy efforts around this issue, co-authoring one of the earliest peer-reviewed articles on outbreak management and giving the first presentation on this topic at the Association's Annual Educational Conference in April 2020.*

References

Abbott, J., Johnson, D., & Wynia, M. (September 21, 2020). Ensuring adequate palliative and hospice care during COVID-19 surges. *JAMA, 324*(14), 1393-1394.

Blanchard, D. (May 26, 2020). Top 10 most dangerous jobs of 2020. *EHS Today*. Retrieved from https://www.ehstoday.com/safety/media-gallery/21132346/top-10-most-dangerous-jobs-of-2020

Centers for Disease Control and Prevention. (December 2020). Information about the Pfizer-BioNTech COVID-19 Vaccine. Retrieved from https://www.cdc.gov/coronavirus/2019-ncov/vaccines/different-vaccines/Pfizer-BioNTech.html

Centers for Medicare & Medicaid Services. (2020). Guidance for infection control and prevention of coronavirus disease 2019 (COVID-19) in nursing homes (revised). Retrieved from https://www.cms.gov/medicareprovider-enrollment-and-certificationsurveycertificationgeninfopolicy-and/guidance-infection-control-and-prevention-coronavirus-disease-2019-covid-19-nursing-homes-revised

Centers for Medicare & Medicaid Services (2020). Percentage of long-stay residents who lose too much weight. In *MDS 3.0 QM Quality Measure Report*. Washington, DC.

Chidambaram, P., Garfield, R., & Neuman, T. (Nov. 25, 2020). COVID-19 has claimed the lives of 100,000 long-term care residents and staff. Retrieved from the Kaiser Family Foundation, https://www.kff.org/policy-watch/covid-19-has-claimed-the-lives-of-100000-long-term-care-residents-and-staff/

Compassion & Choices. Voluntary Stopping of Eating and Drinking (VSED). Retrieved from https://compassionandchoices.org/end-of-life-planning/learn/vsed/

Connole, C. (December 1, 2020). COVID outbreak in nursing homes worst since April. *Provider Magazine*. Retrieved from https://www.providermagazine.com/Breaking-News/Pages/COVID-Outbreak-in-Nursing-Homes-Worst-Since-April.aspx

Creditor, Morton C. (1993). Perspective: Hazards of hospitalization of the elderly. *Annals of Internal Medicine, 118, pp. 219-223.*

Cuomo, A. (2020). Governor's Press Conference, April 28, 2020.

DeSmet, R., Mellaerts, B., Vandewinckele, H., Lybeert, P., Frans, E., Ombelet, S.,…Laurent, M. (2020). Frailty and mortality in hospitalized older adults with COVID-19: Retrospective observational study. *Journal of the American Medical Directors Association, 21*(7), pp. 928-932.

Eaton, J. (2020). Who is to blame? *AARP Bulletin*, December 2020, p. 21.

Ellis, B., & Hicken, M. (2020). Nursing home worker deaths going unscrutinized by federal government. *CNN Investigates*. Atlanta, GA: CNN.

Gandhi, M., Yokoe, D., & Havlir, D. (2020). Asymptomatic transmission, the Achilles' heel of current strategies to control Covid-19. *The New England Journal of Medicine,* 382:2158-2160.

Healy, E. (July 21, 2020). COVID-19 Impact: Clinical trends, advances, and healthcare disparities. Presentation to the Florida Medical Directors Association (FMDA) Journal Club.

Healy, J., Ivory, D., & Kovaleski, S. (October 30, 2020). "A slow killer:" Nursing home residents wither in isolation forced by the virus. *The New York Times.*

McMichael, T. M., Clark, S., Pogosjans, S., Kay, M., Lewis, J., Baer, A.,…CDC COVID-19 Investigation Team. (March 27, 2020). COVID-19 in a long-term care facility — King County, Washington, February 27–March 9, 2020. *Morbidity and Mortality Weekly Report (MMWR), 69*(12): 339-342.

Miltimore, J. (May 7, 2020). How states turned nursing homes into "slaughterhouses" by forcing them to admit discharged COVID-19 patients. *Foundation for Economic Education.*

Parkinson, M. (November 17, 2020). AHCA/NCAL video statement. Retrieved from https://www.ahcancal.org/Pages/default.aspx

Powell, T., & Chuang, E. (2020). COVID in NYC: What we could do better. *The American Journal of Bioethics, Volume 20*, Issue 7, pp. 62-66.

Shao, F., Xu, S., Ma, X., Zhouming, X., Lyu, J., Ng., M.,...Tang, Z. (2020). In-hospital cardiac arrest outcomes among patients with COVID-19 pneumonia in Wuhan, China. *Resuscitation, 151*:18-23.

Tang, O., Bigelow, B., Sheikh, F., Peters, M., Zenilman, J., Bennett, R., & Katz, M. (2020). Outcomes of nursing home COVID-19 patients by initial symptoms and comorbidity: Results of universal testing of 1970 residents. *Journal of the American Medical Directors Association, 21*(12), pp. 1767-1773.

Temkin-Greener, H., Zheng, N. T., Xing, J., & Mukamel, D. B. (2013). Site of death among nursing home residents in the United States: Changing patterns, 2003–2007. *Journal of American Medical Directors Association, (10)*:741–748.

Tresch, D.D., Neahring, J. M., Duthie, E. H., Kartes, S. K., & Aufderheide, T. P. (1993). Outcomes of cardiopulmonary resuscitation in nursing homes: Can we predict who will benefit? *American Journal of Medicine, 95*(2): 123-30.

United States Code (2006). The Public Health and Welfare, Supplement 2, Title 42. U.S.C. 1395i–3: Requirements for, and assuring quality of care in, skilled nursing facilities. Retrieved from https://www.govinfo.gov/app/details/USCODE-2008-title42/USCODE-2008-title42-chap7-subchapXVIII-partA-sec1395i-3/summary

U.S. Department of Health and Human Services. (2019). Long-term care providers and services users in the United States, 2015–2016. *National Center for Health Statistics Vital and Health Statistics*, Series 3, Number 43.

Williams, B. (April 29, 2020). Hospitals are heroic, while nursing homes are always to blame. *McKnight's Long-Term Care News*.

Ye, P., Fry, L., & Champion, J.D. (2020). Changes in advance care planning for nursing home residents during the COVID-19 pandemic. *Journal of the American Medical Directors Association. doi:* https://doi.org/10.1016/j.jamda.2020.11.011.

CHAPTER 6

Voices
The Disparity Between
Personal and Professional Grief:
One Nurse's Story

Brenda Kotar

I became a nurse to help people. It was not an easy undertaking going to nursing school with three little kids, then working the night shift for 7 years while my then-husband was unemployed. Nursing opened my eyes to the suffering of others in a way I could not have imagined. Shortly into my nursing career, I was working three jobs and had gone back to school to get my master's degree in nursing administration. While in graduate school, I lost my best friend and mother unexpectedly. Soon after, I lost my father, which was more expected. Then I lost my marriage, finding myself alone with three kids. I would have liked to say I knew everything there was to know about loss and grieving, but in 2020, I've found myself in a whole new set of circumstances with an even more nuanced perspective on grief.

Once I felt like I had finally landed back on my feet from the whirlwind of personal challenges described above, I found myself living a relatively boring life. My kids were healthy and doing great; one was in college and traveling abroad, one was graduating from high school, and the third was entering his teenage years. Then, COVID-19. My oldest was studying abroad in South Korea as the virus hit Asia; she and I decided it would be best for her to come back home. The world as we knew it soon stopped. I was glued to the news channels and crying for the nurses who were already exhausted by the pandemic, overworked, and given few resources. I felt frustrated. Just one month earlier we had known that the virus was bad in Asia; did the U.S. not get the memo? How could our healthcare system be caught so off guard when even I knew what was coming?

I wondered what I could do to help. After finishing my master's degree, I had made a career change and started teaching nursing. I hadn't worked directly with patients in years, only with my students in their clinical rotations. I thought about ordering sidewalk chalk to write thank-you notes to healthcare workers on my driveway. At exactly the right time, however, the opportunity to fly to New York City to help out in the field presented itself. I jumped at the chance.

I made sure my kids were comfortable with my decision to leave and boarded a plane headed into the unknown. What was I thinking? I had no idea what I was getting myself into; I had never been to New York and knew no one. Thankfully, I was able to quickly find my footing with the other travelers, who were all healthcare workers on the same journey as me. People in health care tend to feel as if we're part of a club, and this was no different, as we instantly began talking about our deployment, where we were staying, and our families back home.

My first days in New York were so difficult. I could barely keep up, which was apparently normal for a crisis. The days were exhausting and the 45-minute bus rides to and from the hotel were taxing; all we wanted to do was eat and go to bed. Yet we found solace in the opportunity to spend the commute talking about our day and what we had witnessed, letting out our frustrations, crying, complaining, and allowing ourselves to be angry. For 21 long days we grieved together, for our patients and for the other nurses who lived there and couldn't leave this nightmare where we were only guests. I loved the people I worked with; they supported us, worked as a team with us, and we all cried together.

When those 21 days were over and I returned home, it was as if I had traveled to outer space. People loved me and called me a hero, saying I must have really made a difference with my patients and saved so many lives. Then why did I feel so miserable? I felt alone, even when I had friends arranging "welcome back" parades on my street and bringing me food every night. I joined a few online Facebook groups with other nurses who had been in New York, but it did not help. It did not help because what I was longing for were those people on the 45-minute bus ride back to the hotel from the long and exhausting shift. I was longing for the comradery of my unplanned support group, the ones I could relate to, the ones who had been through hell with me. But that was all we really had in common. I couldn't just call them up and say "hey, let's talk." I didn't even have their phone numbers. How did I deal with this? I looked for another deployment.

A few months later, I was back at it, this time at a little two-story hospital in Corpus Christi, Texas. The commute was only 10 minutes, so I knew it wouldn't be enough time to bond with the other nurses like I had in New York, but I was grateful for the extra minutes of sleep. On the morning ride, someone took the liberty of saying a prayer in preparation for our shifts. As someone who has been struggling with my faith for years, this took some adjusting for me. Maybe it's the loss I had experienced, or the blood, sweat, and tears I shed for others as a COVID nurse; I'm not sure, but that morning prayer became my time—my time to listen and appreciate what someone else was doing for me. It was everything I had been craving but didn't know I needed. I made sure to thank the nurse who said that prayer every morning and let her know how much it helped me to get through each day, because in Texas I wasn't saving lives, and I did not feel like a hero.

My patients were so sick, and every day seemed like the day before. Patient gets admitted on 4 liters nasal cannula; a few days later they are maxed out on 15 liters non-rebreather and I am calling the respiratory therapist about getting a BiPAP. If we couldn't get a BiPAP initiated quickly enough, the patient's heart would stop, and we would start compressions. One day I was tasked with giving our last BiPAP to one of two patients who needed it. This was never a decision I ever imagined making as a nurse, and I had to make it with no time to think or reason. I will never know if I ended up making the "right" decision, because both patients ultimately died.

So many of my patients were tired, expressing to me that they didn't want to fight anymore. Yet their families would tell us to do everything we could for them. The communication was difficult, with the patient wanting one thing and the family wanting another, the patient too sick to talk to their family, and the family unable to visit. I became the middleman between my patients and their families during one of the worst situations a person can experience. I had a patient that needed a Do Not Resuscitate (DNR) order explained and signed. I had never explained a DNR to a patient or had a patient sign one, but the doctor said he didn't have time to do it himself. I will never forget the look on her face when I explained it and she signed it; she died that night, alone, no family at her bedside, only a nurse. The stories on the news show heartbreaking scenes of goodbyes said through iPads. The hospitals I worked at had no iPads; they were too expensive.

The grief I have encountered with COVID-19 care is complicated. It's different from the personal loss I have experienced. I grieve for the loss of my many patients, over and over again, since I had no time to stop and breathe while I was in the thick of it. The grief comes again when there is time to think and process the last 6 months. This is where I am today, making the tough and conscious decision to get going each day, to tackle the mundane challenges and to move on. Some days are better than others, but it is always lonely, even being surrounded by all the best people who have always been there. I will always miss my unplanned support group on those bus rides and think of them daily. I have started praying again and am working on my relationship with God. I celebrate the lives of those who we have lost and do my best not to take anything for granted. I get up and continue to live my mundane, peaceful life in honor of those who no longer can. Life is a gift and ours is worth living, just as theirs were.

Brenda Kotar, RN, MSN, is a nurse with over 15 years of experience working in pediatrics and with adults. She is passionate about her current role as a nursing instructor for Metropolitan Community College Nursing School in Kansas City, MO. She lives in Prairie Village, KS, and enjoys vacationing with her kids and socializing with friends. In 2020, she spent a significant amount of time in New York City and Corpus Christi, TX, caring for COVID-19 patients. Since writing this piece, she left for Amarillo, TX, for her third COVID-19 deployment.

CHAPTER 7

When Grief Goes Viral: Psychological Impacts of the COVID-19 Pandemic

Robert A. Neimeyer and Sherman A. Lee

Andrew and Karen scheduled a telehealth session with their therapist when they confronted a seemingly insoluble dilemma. Their teenage daughter Lindsey had developed a fever and had just tested positive for COVID-19 and both parents anguished over the decision of whether to seek her admission to the hospital or to return her to their home, which they shared with Karen's 67-year-old mother with a history of respiratory problems. The family was paralyzed by an agonizing decision—hospitalizing Lindsey in a facility where they could not even visit her or placing her grandmother in an eldercare facility, at high risk of infection and associated mortality, to protect her from risk of near certain infection in the family home. Compounding their spiraling anxiety about abandoning either of their loved ones were the struggles they faced with the required distance learning for their restless and angry preteen son and Andrew's protracted joblessness with the closure of the restaurant in which he had worked for the past 4 years.

* * *

Tynea had always been close to her mother JoAnn, who had singlehandedly raised her and her four siblings, serving as a strong role model and a pillar of her church community. But this "larger than life" woman had recently experienced an incurable relapse of her cancer and had been admitted to the hospital, where strict precautions to protect healthcare staff and patients from exposure to the coronavirus made it impossible for Tynea to visit JoAnn during the weeks of her final hospitalization. On those rare occasions when a harried nurse could hold a phone in front of her for a few minutes, Tynea reflected, "The words and images come through, but the feeling doesn't." When JoAnn died alone in the facility, only one person out of a family of over 40 members was permitted to attend the funeral—Tynea. The brief graveside service by the overworked pastor did little to assuage her grief and left her feeling that she had failed even to provide her mother a proper homegoing.

A novel coronavirus that emerged from Wuhan, China in late 2019 quickly spread around the world, causing chaos, panic, and death everywhere it reached. Among the innumerable losses caused by the pandemic were the massive work and school closures implemented to contain its spread. In less than one month after COVID-19 was declared a pandemic by the World Health Organization, the jobless rate in America rose from a steady 3.5% to an unprecedented high of nearly 15% (Trading Economics, 2020). Ninety-four percent of the world's students experienced school closures, making this the largest disruption of education systems in history (United Nations, 2020). To make matters worse, public health issues such as domestic violence (WHO, 2020) and drug overdoses (American Medical Association, 2020) have also increased during the infectious disease outbreak. Understandably, the COVID-19 pandemic has taken a serious toll on the mental health and wellbeing of people around the globe.

Our goal in this chapter is to summarize what is known about the psychological impacts of the pandemic in light of the countless death and nondeath losses it has brought in its wake. In particular, we will focus on the disproportionate impact on two vulnerable communities—healthcare workers and people of color in the United States—whose higher risks of infection translate directly into higher levels of coronavirus anxiety, depression, and, given their higher COVID-19 mortality, complicated bereavement. We will underscore how evidence-based risk factors for prolonged and disabling grief closely match the circumstances of most deaths occurring during the pandemic, even when they arise from other causes. Finally, we will close by offering a few principles to guide therapists assisting clients struggling in the shadow of these losses and point readers toward further resources for assessment and intervention.

PSYCHOLOGICAL EFFECTS OF THE PANDEMIC

Prior to the COVID-19 pandemic, depression and anxiety disorders were already quite prevalent globally. In 2015, the proportion of the world's population with depressive disorders was estimated to be at

4.4%, while anxiety disorders estimates were slightly lower around 3.6% (WHO, 2017). During the first months of the pandemic, however, an astonishing 24.4% of Americans reported clinical levels of depression, while 29.8% reported clinical levels of anxiety (CDC, 2020). The gravity of these statistics is underscored when one considers that depression is the single largest contributor to disability globally and one of the major contributors to suicide around the world (WHO, 2017). And although anxiety is not a major contributor to suicide deaths, it is strongly associated with suicide attempts. For instance, in a national epidemiological survey of Americans, over 70% of people with a lifetime history of suicide attempts were found to also have an anxiety disorder (Nepon et al., 2010).

Coronavirus Anxiety

Beyond the generalized anxiety studied by many investigators are the specific fears and anxieties over the coronavirus itself. For instance, Lee and his colleagues (Lee, 2020; Lee et al., 2020b) carefully evaluated a large set of cognitive, emotional, behavioral, and physiological symptoms of anxiety that people endorsed with reference to the coronavirus; identified a coherent set of self-reported physiological symptoms (e.g., sleep disruption, loss of appetite, nausea) that seemed to best capture this distinctive form of distress; and established an optimized cut score of ≥ 9 beyond which it was highly predictive of substantial impairments in work and social functioning. Clinicians are encouraged to use the Coronavirus Anxiety Scale 2.0 included on the next page to screen for such need in practice settings, as well as to include it in research without any special permission, simply citing the original source of the scale (Milman et al., 2020).

Coronavirus Anxiety Scale 2.0 (CAS 2.0)

How often have you experienced the following activities over the last week?	Never	Rarely, 1-2 days	Sometimes, 3-4 days	Often, 5-6 days	Every day
1. I felt dizzy, lightheaded, or faint, when I read or listened to news about the coronavirus.	0	1	2	3	4
2. I had trouble falling or staying asleep because I was thinking about the coronavirus.	0	1	2	3	4
3. I felt paralyzed or frozen when I thought about or was exposed to information about the coronavirus.	0	1	2	3	4
4. I lost interest in eating when I thought about or was exposed to information about the coronavirus.	0	1	2	3	4
5. I felt nauseous or had stomach problems when I thought about or was exposed to information about the coronavirus.	0	1	2	3	4
Column Totals	___ +	___ +	___ +	___ +	___ +

Total Score [   ]

Note. The CAS 2.0 is placed in the public domain to encourage its use in clinical assessment and research. No formal permission is therefore required for its reproduction and use by others, beyond appropriate citation of the original article (Source: Milman et al., 2020).

Although this subjective experience of nearly unverbalizable somatic distress warrants attention in its own right, coronavirus anxiety also has been linked to negative religious coping (viewing the pandemic as a form of divine punishment), drug and alcohol use, hopelessness, and suicidal ideation. In fact, coronavirus anxiety has had such a profound effect on people's state of mind during the pandemic that is has been shown to predict depression, generalized anxiety, and social and work adjustment, beyond personality traits and COVID-19 factors such as exposure or illness (Lee & Crunk, 2020; Lee et al., 2020a). Perhaps the most disturbing outcome of coronavirus-related fear has been its link to suicide deaths. In a study of sixty-nine suicide cases in India, the most prominent causal factor was fear of COVID-19 (Dsousa et al., 2020).

What might account for the pernicious effect of the pandemic on mental health outcomes? One explanation is the extent to which it violates people's assumptive world by challenging the predictability and meaningfulness of their lives, their sense of justice, and their ability to control relevant outcomes. Milman et al. (2020) found that the violation of such core beliefs was strongly predictive of coronavirus anxiety, and that adherence to social distancing policies appeared to mitigate such distress by helping to preserve people's sense of agency, comprehensibility, and "footing in the world" in otherwise threatening times. We will return to the implications of these findings when we turn to the topic of intervention below.

Given the gravity of the situation, it is vital that mental health professionals efficiently screen and treat individuals who are suffering from this form of pandemic-related psychopathology. As one contribution toward this effort, the most recent version of the Coronavirus Anxiety Scale (the CAS 2.0) (Milman et al., 2020) is included in this chapter for unrestricted use by health and mental health workers and researchers.

Communities of Color

Although the COVID-19 pandemic has made life difficult for most people, the mental health consequences have been particularly evident for communities of color. According to national surveys of Americans during the pandemic, Latinos and Blacks reported higher levels of anxiety, depression, and suicidality compared to their white counterparts (CDC, 2020; Fitzpatrick et al., 2020). These heightened stresses and concerns make sense when one considers the fact that the infection and death rates in Black communities are three-fold and six-fold higher, respectively, than white communities in the US (Yancy, 2020). Latinos, comprising 18% of the population, account for 33% of all confirmed cases of COVID-19 and 20% of all COVID-19 related deaths (Couch et al., 2020). Longstanding disparities in work conditions and access to health care may account for much of these numbers. For instance, a large proportion of people of color work in high-risk settings such as farms, factories, grocery stores, hospitals, transportation, and service industries where frequent and close contact with the public and coworkers increases their risk of COVID-19 exposure. This problem is further compounded by the fact that people of color often have little to no option of avoiding these environments. For example, Blacks are 35% less likely to work from home than whites, while Latinos are 50% less likely than whites to have this option (Treisman, 2020). Moreover, many people of color who did get sick during the pandemic did not seek health care because they did not have health insurance and/or the funds to pay for such costly services. Perhaps one of the most shocking examples of the disproportionate impact of the pandemic on communities of color were mortality rates among children. Specifically, 74% of children who died from COVID-19 in America were Black and Latino (Bixler et al., 2020). Unfortunately, stresses regarding inequality and the rising tensions regarding racism have magnified pandemic-related problems for communities of color who are experiencing a mental health emergency.

Healthcare Workers

Healthcare workers as a group are particularly vulnerable to a wide range of physical and psychological problems during pandemics. Not only are the stresses and traumatic experiences of working with people infected with a dangerous virus high among healthcare workers, but the long hours of work, continual concerns over infection, and lack of emotional support also contribute to their already compromised mental condition during infectious disease outbreaks. For example, in a recent meta-analysis of studies that examined healthcare workers during the current and past coronavirus outbreaks, the most frequent psychological issues reported were concerns over general health (62.5%), followed by fear of infection (43.7%), insomnia (37.9%), psychological distress (37.8%), burnout (34.4%), anxiety (29.0%), depression (26.3%), posttraumatic stress (20.7%), somatization (16.1%), and stigmatization (14%) (Salazar de Pablo et al., 2020). Among healthcare workers, however, frontline medical workers may be at the greatest risk for psychological morbidities as they are more directly and more frequently exposed to life-threatening, traumatic, and emotionally exhausting situations than their counterparts. For example, in a case-controlled study that compared 1,173 frontline healthcare workers in China with a demographically similar group of 1,173 nonfrontline healthcare workers, frontline healthcare workers had higher rates of any mental problem (52.6% vs. 34.0%), anxiety symptoms (15.7% vs. 7.4%), and insomnia (47.8% vs. 29.1%) than nonfrontline healthcare workers (Cai et al., 2020). As healthcare workers are essential to our fight against infectious diseases and other medical concerns, it is important that their mental health needs be met with an immediate, tailored, and effective response.

GRIEF IN THE CONTEXT OF COVID-19

Of the numerous social, economic, and medical impacts of the pandemic, the fatalities resulting from its global spread are the starkest. As this chapter goes to press, the world is approaching well over 81 million documented infections and close to 2 million deaths from COVID-19 (WHO, Dec. 31, 2020). Precisely as predicted by demographic microsimulation forecasts in the earliest weeks of the pandemic, this tsunami of loss raises the specter of "the collateral damage that this level of mortality would exact," making it "important that the burden of bereavement, and its potential mental and physical health consequences, is factored into…the public health challenge facing all nations" (Verdery & Smith-Greenway, 2020, p. 2). For mental health professionals, awareness of the risks for complicated grief associated with such losses is a compelling necessity.

Recognizing this, Lee and Neimeyer (2020) rigorously evaluated dozens of potential symptoms of pandemic grief administered to over 800 people who had lost loved ones to COVID-19 and developed an efficient and validated 5-item screener for dysfunctional response to bereavement, the Pandemic Grief Scale (PGS). A score of ≥ 7 on the PGS was found to identify mourners struggling with work and social impairment as a function of their grief far more effectively than general measures of depression and general anxiety. Alarmingly, over 66% of those bereaved scored in the clinical range, suggesting the critical importance of screening for survivors of COVID losses who could benefit from early intervention through grief therapy. Clinicians are encouraged to use the PGS included on the next page to screen for such need in practice settings, as well as to include it in research without any special permission, simply citing the original source of the scale (Lee & Neimeyer, 2020).

Pandemic Grief Scale (PGS)

Over the last 2 weeks, how often have you experienced the following thoughts, feelings, or behaviors related to your loss?	Not at all	Several days	More than half the days	Nearly everyday
1. I wished to die in order to be with the deceased.	0	1	2	3
2. I experienced confusion over my role in life or felt like my identity was diminished because of the loss.	0	1	2	3
3. Nothing seemed to matter much to me because of this loss.	0	1	2	3
4. I found it difficult to have positive memories about the deceased.	0	1	2	3
5. I believed that without the deceased, life was either meaningless, empty, or could not go on.	0	1	2	3
Column Totals	_____ +	_____ +	_____ +	_____ +

Total Score [ ]

Note. The PGS is placed in the public domain to encourage its use in clinical assessment and research. No formal permission is therefore required for its reproduction and use by others, beyond appropriate citation of the original article (Lee & Neimeyer, 2020).

Just how long lasting the dysfunctional grief identified by the PGS will be awaits longitudinal research. But there is reason for considerable concern that mourners who display this response to COVID-19 loss could be at elevated risk of Prolonged Grief Disorder (WHO, 2019), a stress-related condition clearly distinguishable from adaptive grieving. In this form of life-vitiating response to loss, mourners struggle with turbulent emotions of longing, guilt, loneliness, and desolation which impair their ability to function in the contexts of family, work, and the social world for many months beyond the death, and often years.

Moreover, this condition carries real health risks for a variety of stress-related disorders, cardiac problems, addictions, immune system dysfunction, impaired quality of life, and even suicide (Maerker et al., 2016). The COVID-19 context of dying presents a perfect storm of converging forces that greatly exacerbate the likelihood of prolonged grief in its aftermath.

Risk Factors for Complicated Grief in the Pandemic

In the past 20 years, a great deal has been learned about risk factors for bereavement complications, which include social isolation, unexpectedness of the death, lower education or socioeconomic disadvantage in the mourner, insecure and anxious attachment, spiritual struggle in bereavement, inability to make sense of the loss, and lack of institutional and informational support in the care facility in which the death takes place (Neimeyer & Burke, 2017). Significantly, every one of these factors characterizes deaths that occur in the context of the current pandemic, whether or not they result from COVID-19 or other causes. Family and close friends of patients are typically isolated from their loved ones at the end of life in an effort to mitigate contagion, reversing decades of progressive policies that previously encouraged family caregiving. Social distancing protocols combined with travel bans further isolate mourners from one another, even during funerals and memorial services, which commonly are performed online, postponed indefinitely, or foregone altogether. Especially for the vulnerable elderly or those with compromised health conditions, COVID-19 deaths commonly come suddenly, within mere days or weeks of diagnosis, even with respiratory support. As noted above, coronavirus fatalities disproportionately are concentrated among economically disadvantaged communities of color. Inability to offer comfort and touch at the bedside of the dying challenges attachment imperatives to draw close to loved ones, leaving a heavy burden of helplessness, shame, and guilt. Religiously oriented mourners may question the beneficence, power, or intentions of a God they once trusted to care for them and their loved ones, while struggling with estrangement from spiritual communities shuttered during the pandemic. Core elements of people's assumptive worlds and the sense that life is predictable, controllable, just, and meaningful are undermined by the pandemic in general, and the context of dying in particular. And overwhelmed healthcare facilities rarely have the luxury to attend to family needs, as they bend efforts toward urgent care of severely ill patients, while attempting to protect the health of their residents and staff. The consequences are entirely predictable: as the months roll forward, the incidence of prolonged grief among those bereaved by any cause in the pandemic can be expected to skyrocket well above the incidence rate of 10% documented in pre-pandemic times (Lundorff et al., 2017).

Unfinished Business in Bereavement

The common denominator of all of the above risk factors is their contribution to "unfinished business" in bereavement, those unresolved relational issues between the living and the dead that defy well-meaning advice by friends, family, and sometimes therapists to "move on" (Klingspon et al., 2015). Research has identified two thematic clusters of concern yielding psychometrically clear subscales on a carefully validated measure of the construct, the *Unfinished Business in Bereavement Scale* (UBBS) (Holland et al., 2020). These include *Unfulfilled Wishes* (e.g., I wish I could have attended to ___'s needs more closely in his/her final days; I wish I had told ___ how much s/he meant to me) and *Unresolved Conflict* (e.g., I never got a chance to resolve a breach in our relationship; I wish I had had the chance to tell ___ that I forgive him/her). Taken together with the meaning made of the loss, unfinished business accounts for 50-60% of the variance in complicated grief symptomatology (Holland et al., 2020), and is especially likely to arise in immediate family relationships (Klingspon et al., 2015).

IMPLICATIONS FOR PRACTICE

The evidence reviewed here underscores the value of assessing the general psychological impact and specific anxieties associated with the coronavirus pandemic, as well as the presence of bereavement complications such as dysfunctional, prolonged, and incapacitating grief. Optimally, such assessments would take place in all healthcare and mental health settings to which people present for care. A further obvious injunction for practicing counselors would be to assess such potent predictors of prolonged grief as challenges to meaning or unresolved relational issues and to introduce these themes into the work of therapy. Beyond using the validated scales for this purpose noted earlier, open probes in the therapeutic session (e.g., *What did you once believe about life that you no longer are so sure of? Are there things that you would want to express or work out with your loved one if you had the chance?*) Can bring to light issues deserving attention and open the door to the appropriate selection of therapeutic procedures. These might include restorative retelling of the loss, directed journaling, and expressive arts approaches to promote meaning making, as well as imaginal dialogues, creative rituals of remembrance, and legacy projects to address unresolved relational issues with the deceased (Neimeyer, 2012; 2016). Ironically, the pandemic itself can afford opportunities for helping clients reaffirm an assumptive world that has been challenged in its aftermath, as responsible adherence to social mitigation practices has been found to predict conservation or restoration of core beliefs in predictability, control, and self-agency, thereby mitigating anxieties associated with the COVID-19 crisis (Milman et al., 2020).

Unfortunately, however, developing competence in the existential work of rebuilding worlds of meaning shattered by loss and restoring a sense of attachment security with the dead are rarely given space in graduate curricula, and hence call for further professional development through ongoing professional continuing education. Given the predictably high demand for professional level grief therapy arising from the current and future pandemics, we hope that readers will join us in embracing this challenge.

Robert A. Neimeyer, PhD, is Professor Emeritus of the Department of Psychology, University of Memphis; maintains an active consulting and coaching practice; and also directs the Portland Institute for Loss and Transition, where he oversees extensive online and onsite professional training modules. Neimeyer has published 30 books, including Routledge's series on Techniques of Grief Therapy, *and serves as Editor of* Death Studies. *The author of over 500 articles and chapters and a popular workshop presenter, he is currently working to advance a more adequate theory of grieving as a meaning-making process. In recognition of his contributions, he has been given Lifetime Achievement Awards by both the Association for Death Education and Counseling and the International Network on Personal Meaning.*

Sherman A. Lee, PhD, is an associate professor of psychology at Christopher Newport University. Lee studies negative feeling states, such as anxiety and grief, and the role personality and religion play in those emotional experiences. He also teaches courses in the psychology of personality, psychology of the human-animal bond (Anthrozoology), and the psychology of death, dying, and bereavement (Thanatology). The creator of the Trait Sympathy Scales, Islamophobia Scale, Persistent Complex Bereavement Inventory, *and the* Coronavirus Anxiety Scale, *he is currently researching the impact of the COVID-19 pandemic on the psychological well-being of people around the world.*

REFERENCES

American Medical Association. (September 8, 2020). *Issue brief: Reports of increases in opioid-related overdose and other concerns during COVID pandemic,* 1-15.

Bixler, D., Miller, A., Mattison, C., Taylor, B., Komatsu, K., Pompa, X. P.,…Pediatric Morality Investigation Team. (2020). SARS-CoV-2–Associated Deaths Among Persons Aged <21 Years United States, February 12–July 31, 2020. *Morbidity and Mortality Weekly Report.* http://dx.doi.org/10.15585/mmwr.mm6937e4

Cai, Q., Feng, H., Huang, J., Wang, M., Lu, X., Xie, Y.,…Liu, Y. (2020). The mental health of frontline and non-frontline medical workers during the Coronavirus disease 2019 (COVID-19) outbreak in China: A case-control study. *Journal of Affective Disorders.* https://doi.org/10.1016/j.jad.2020.06.031

Centers for Disease Control and Prevention. (2020). *Household pulse survey: Indicators of anxiety or depression.* https://www.cdc.gov/nchs/covid19/pulse/mental-health.htm

Couch, K. A., Fairle, R. W., & Xu, H. (May 18, 2020). *The impacts of COVID-19 on minority unemployment: First evidence from April 2020 CPS Microdata.* http://dx.doi.org/10.2139/ssrn.3604814

Dsousa, D. D., Quadros, S., Hyderbadwala, Z. J., & Mamun, M. A. (2020). Aggregated COVID-19 suicide incidences in India: Fear of COVID-19 infection is the prominent causative factor. *Psychiatry Research, 290.* https://doi.org/10.1016/j.psychres.2020.113145

Fitzpatrick, K. M., Harris, C., & Drawve, G. (2020). How bad is it? Suicidality in the middle of the COVID-19 pandemic. *Suicide and Life-Threatening Behavior.* https://doi.org/10.1111/sltb.12655

Holland, J. M., Klingspon, K. L., Lichtenthal, W. G., & Neimeyer, R. A. (2020). The Unfinished Business in Bereavement Scale (UBBS): Development and psychometric evaluation. *Death Studies, 44*, 65-77. doi: 10.1080/07481187.2018.1521101

Klingspon, K. L., Holland, J. M., Neimeyer, R. A., & Lichtenthal, W. G. (2015). Unfinished business in bereavement. *Death Studies, 39*, 387-398. doi: 10.1080/07481187.2015.1029143

Lee, S. A. (2020). Coronavirus Anxiety Scale: A brief mental health screener for COVID-19 related anxiety. *Death Studies, 44*(7), 393-401. https://doi.org/10.1080/ 07481187.2020.1748481

Lee, S. A., & Crunk, A. E. (2020). Fear and psychopathology during the COVID-19 crisis: Neuroticism, hypochondriasis, reassurance-seeking, and coronaphobia as fear factors. *OMEGA – Journal of Death and Dying.* doi.org/10.1177/0030222820949350

Lee, S. A., Jobe, M. C., Mathis, A. A., & Gibbons, J. A. (2020a). Incremental validity of coronaphobia: Coronavirus anxiety explains depression, generalized anxiety, and death anxiety. *Journal of Anxiety Disorders, 74.* doi.org/10.1016/j.janxdis.2020.102268

Lee, S. A., Mathis, A. A., Jobe, M. C., & Pappalardo, E. A. (2020b). Clinically significant fear and anxiety of COVID-19: A psychometric examination of the Coronavirus Anxiety Scale. *Psychiatry Research, 290.* doi.org/10.1016/j.psychres.2020.113112

Lee, S. A., & Neimeyer, R. A. (2020). Pandemic Grief Scale: A screening tool for dysfunctional grief due to a COVID-19 Loss. *Death Studies,* doi.org/10.1080/07481187.2020.1853885

Lundorff, M., Holmgren, H., Zachariae, R., Farver-Vestergaard, I., & O'Connor, M. (2017). Prevalence of prolonged grief disorder in adult bereavement: A systematic review and meta-analysis. *Journal of Affective Disorders, 212*, 138-149.

Maercker, A., Neimeyer, R. A., & Simiola, V. (2016). Depression and complicated grief. In J. Cook, S. Gold, & C. Dalenberg (Eds.). *APA handbook of trauma psychology.* Washington, DC: American Psychological Association.

Milman, E., Lee, S. A., & Neimeyer, R. A. (2020). Social isolation and the mitigation of coronavirus anxiety: The mediating role of meaning. *Death Studies*. doi.org/10.1080/07481187.2020.1775362

Neimeyer, R. A. (Ed.). (2016). *Techniques of grief therapy: Assessment and intervention.* Philadelphia, PA: Routledge.

Neimeyer, R. A. (Ed.). (2012). *Techniques of grief therapy: Creative practices for counseling the bereaved.* Philadelphia, PA: Routledge.

Neimeyer, R. A., & Burke, L. A. (2017). What makes grief complicated? Risk factors for complications in bereavement. In K. J. Doka & A. S. Tucci (Eds.), *Living with grief: When grief is complicated.* Washington, DC: Hospice Foundation of America.

Nepon, J., Belik, S., Bolton, J., & Sareen, J. (2010). The relationship between anxiety disorders and suicide attempts: Findings from the National Epidemiologic Survey on Alcohol and Related Conditions. *Depression & Anxiety, 27*(9), 791-798. doi.org/10.1002/da.20674

Salazar de Pablo, G., Vaquerizo-Serrano, J., Catalan, A., Arango, C., Moreno, C., Ferre, F.,...Fusar-Poli, P. (2020). Impact of coronavirus syndromes on physical and mental health of health care workers: Systematic review and meta-analysis. *Journal of Affective Disorders, 275*, 48-57. doi.org/10.1016/j.jad.2020.06.022

Trading Economics (2020, September 5*). United States unemployment rate.* https://tradingeconomics.com/united-states/unemployment-rate

Treisman, R. (2020). CDC study finds Hispanics hit disproportionately hard by workplace outbreaks. https://www.npr.org/sections/coronavirus-live-updates/2020/08/17/903313535/cdcstudy-finds-hispanics-hit-disproportionately-hard-by-workplace-outbreaks

United Nations (2020, August). *Policy brief: Education during COVID-19 and beyond,* 1-26.

Verdery, A. M., & Smith-Greenway, E. (2020). COVID-19 and family bereavement in the United States. *Applied Demography Newsletter, 32*, 1-2.

World Health Organization (2017). *Depression and other common mental disorders: Global health estimates,* 1-24.

World Health Organization (2019). *International Classification of Disease, 11th Edition: Prolonged Grief Disorder*. https://icd.who.int/browse11/l-m/en#/http://id.who.int/icd/entity/1183832314

World Health Organization (September 5, 2020). *Numbers at a glance*. https://www.who.int/emergencies/diseases/novel-coronavirus-2019

World Health Organization (WHO). (2020). WHO coronavirus disease (COVID-19) dashboard. Retrieved December 31, 2020 from https://covid19.who.int/

Yancy, C. W. (2020). COVID-19 and African Americans. *JAMA*, *323*(19), 1891-1892. doi:10.1001/jama.2020.6548

CHAPTER 8

Voices
In it for the Long Haul

Lisa O'Brien

Life never happens the way we expect; that's something I've been reminded of over and over this past year. And even though I know this to be true, it's still hard to believe that I started 2020 off on the beaches of Hawaii, taking pictures of sea turtles and snorkeling in the reef. Yet here I am, ending the year writing a story focused on grief.

COVID-19 was the unwanted souvenir that I somehow brought home with me from Hawaii, back in the early part of March 2020. It was the week before the country shut down; masks and social distancing weren't even a thing yet. At that point all we knew about COVID-19 was that it showed up with a cough, fever, shortness of breath, and the outcome was binary; either you survived it or you didn't.

My case was "mild" to begin with and I thought I had mostly kicked it by week 5 except for a few lingering symptoms. I started walking every day to regain some strength and prevent pneumonia. But by week 8 everything changed, and I'm still not sure how I lived through what followed. I started experiencing erratic heart rates that would spike just from standing up. I felt a buzzing vibration daily that traveled through my whole body and random adrenaline rushes would wake me up every night when my body started forgetting to breathe. By the end of month 3, I had developed a blood clot in my arm and a week later one developed in my lung. My symptoms were never the same from day to day and new ones would constantly appear. For months, I cycled through over 50 different symptoms, leaving no body system untouched; I experienced rashes, insomnia, tingling in my hands and feet, fatigue, short-term memory loss, shortness of breath, blurry vision, irregular heart rates and blood pressure readings, and the list goes on.

Throughout the months that my symptoms were the worst I wondered how I could go on with a body so full of dysfunction that it no longer felt like my own. I developed a newfound empathy for those who have lived with chronic illness for decades, something that I previously hadn't thought much about. Initially the doctors who I saw were completely baffled by my symptoms. They couldn't tell me why COVID-19 affected me this way and they didn't know when, or if, I would ever go back to who I was. This left me feeling lost. If the medical community didn't know what was wrong with me, where else could I turn?

In the beginning my health concerns were regularly dismissed and lots of times I was told that healing would "just take time," an uncertainty dressed up like reassurance. Some of my healthcare providers pointed towards the possible decline of my mental health, believing that was where my struggle must lie, but I knew there had to be more to it. Other times, I was met with disbelief, not only from healthcare providers, but also family and friends from whom I craved understanding and support.

Some of my biggest supporters became those in the post-COVID-19 support groups that I discovered. They were strangers from around the world, but instantly felt like old friends. We were desperate for answers and begging to be seen and heard while facing the possible chronicity of an illness that was only supposed to last no longer than 14 days. Somehow, we had ended up in it for the "long haul," and over time we became known as The Long Haulers. Finding the support groups was a breath of fresh air. The stories were filled with suffering, but at the same time they legitimized the bizarre symptoms that had plagued my body for weeks. It was then that I knew I wasn't crazy and that I wasn't alone.

While I'm extremely grateful that I'm still alive, there are times that I grieve for what COVID-19 stole from me. Parts of my identity started to slip away as I lost my independence. I could no longer be the mom I used to be or the friend I once was. For months I could barely get out of bed most days; I had to use a chair to take a shower, and my teenage children had to start driving me to all my doctor appointments because I no longer trusted my body to behave the way it should.

Sure, I survived COVID-19, but in many aspects, I lost my life; a life I had hoped to live and a life I loved, filled with travel, excitement, and adventure. The year before I got sick, I had rafted down the Green River, sunbathed on the beaches of Puerto Rico, and hiked on snowy slick rock to the Arches in Moab. Several months before I got ill, I had begun to learn Irish dancing and had just started to perfect the steps to an Irish jig. Now the dance shoes that I ordered before the world shut down still sit at the dance studio and my new matching suitcases have sat empty for almost a year. Sometimes it feels like my old life is still within my grasp if only I could just turn a few more corners; other times it feels a million miles away, like I may never get back there, to the person I once was.

COVID-19 also took my health, something that I think we all take for granted until it's gone. It's still uncertain if I will ever regain it back 100% or if this will be my new normal from now on. There are days that I'm angry and think, "Why did this happen to me? Why did others get an easier version of COVID-19 with a complete recovery, while I am still struggling along with thousands of others, almost a year later?" When the pandemic ends many will go back to their normal lives, but I might not get to go back to mine. This feels unfair, like life often does, but then I look at what I've accomplished and gained because of COVID-19 and it leads me to acceptance through a perspective of hope.

Because of COVID-19 I have gained countless friends across the country; compassionate, loving people that never would have crossed my path had I not gotten sick. We keep each other going on the hardest days, the days when knowing you aren't alone count the most. Because of COVID-19, I'm not the same person that I once was; none of us are, and maybe that's ok. In some ways I may be weaker than I was, but in countless ways I've gained so much strength. I have started a local support group and found a few thousand others in my own community who are struggling to regain a life they once loved. I've raised awareness by sharing my story through every local media outlet I could, along with other brave souls from my group who have shared theirs as well. I've learned that it doesn't matter what people think of me as long as my message reaches the people it needs to. I've connected with researchers and medical professionals and found the ones who will listen to us and want to help us. These professionals have created support groups for us and are finding ways to fund and start research. In early 2021, a new post-COVID-19 care clinic will open at our local hospital, something we've pushed for since August 2020. Advocating while still recovering has been exhilarating and exhausting, but I'm determined to make sure that we all have the best chance to come out whole on the other side.

They say that there's beauty, joy, and hope woven into any suffering or strife. The good is there and we just have to find it.

Lisa O'Brien works as a Financial Programs Analyst within the federal sector. Prior to that, she spent close to 20 years in various positions working for the U.S. Postal Service. She is the founder of the Utah COVID-19 Long Haulers group and advocates for those dealing with the long-term effects of COVID-19. Her group serves as a place for other Utahns to find resources for their prolonged COVID-19 recoveries and receive support from other Long Haulers living in Utah. She holds two master's degrees from Western Governors University. O'Brien is a lover of travel and (when there is not a pandemic) tries to travel once a month, even if it's just somewhere within Utah. She also loves reading, cooking, hiking, kayaking, and camping. She has two amazing kids who are young adults and enjoys watching them forge their own paths into adulthood.

CHAPTER 9

Grief Groups in 2020: Transitioning to a Virtual Platform

Maria Georgopoulos

For many, the early days of the COVID-19 pandemic came with a flurry of activity to locate economic stability, food, and safety, setting aside the emotional impact of it all to focus on survival. But for grievers, the intensity of emotions and vulnerability could not be put aside. Grief can cause people to feel unsafe, as their assumptions of a predictable world are shattered in the wake of death. The additional threat of a very real pandemic that could harm them or claim the lives of more people they love has escalated levels of distress for many.

Many of the families that we as bereavement counselors and other clinicians serve were fearful that their bereavement groups would come to an end. The families wondered how they would navigate an already isolating grief journey in a new world order that required further isolation. As clinicians, we wondered the same, and found ourselves faced with a number of our own questions. How would we respond to the intensified needs of our current families as well as accommodate the countless individuals who were now calling to request bereavement support in the wake of a COVID-19 death in their lives? People we served were in a state of panic as the emotional toll of yielding and adjusting to the chaos around them was starting to weigh heavily in the midst of their grief.

Virtual groups were born out of need, just as other counseling services have developed over the years due to changes and demand. Video conferencing was the most feasible way to move forward, despite the hesitations we all had. Many of us chose our careers for the intimacy embedded in them, and our traditional training guided us in attuning to clients through the use of verbal and nonverbal communication.

How would that, and other therapeutic aspects of providing support, change in the virtual world? Ready or not, we now needed to learn. Here are some lessons that I have learned, some challenges I've had to address, and some opportunities I have seen, to help you as a clinician in providing grief support in this new way.

Of the many different virtual platforms, our organization chose to move forward with Zoom. It is one of the most utilized platforms, and many of our existing members already had some knowledge of it. We purchased several corporate plans to provide our members with the highest level of confidentiality. As clinicians consider which platform to use, consulting with state mental health governing bodies is a good start in order to determine telehealth rules and regulations before proceeding.

Intakes are always important to complete but especially so when facilitating virtual support groups. Many grievers may have never been in a support group, much less a virtual one. Collecting pertinent background information such as mental health history and obtaining emergency contact information, such as the client's physical address and the name of a local hospital, assists with being able to assess group readiness and facilitate communication in case a member is having a crisis. Intakes also provide a space to review standard and virtual group guidelines with participants in order to facilitate group readiness. Offering an individual online tutorial prior to the start of group for those who need practice connecting to the virtual platform can be useful.

Due to the nature of virtual groups, some attendees may present themselves in more informal ways or engage in behaviors that they would not normally if the groups were in person. Some behaviors may be quite distracting, such as cooking, walking around the house, or cleaning while in the group. Other behaviors can be concerning, such as drinking alcohol or smoking, while in the group. To help manage distracting behaviors, starting each group session with some basic guidelines can be a helpful reminder:

- Remember to keep your environment free of distractions and to remain attentive to group discussions.
- Please arrive on time and plan on staying the entire length of group.

- Please refrain from behaviors you would not engage in if we were meeting in person, such as drinking alcohol or smoking cigarettes during group time.
- Join the group in a space where others around you cannot easily hear what you or anyone else is saying in the group to maintain confidentiality. If you don't have a private space to join the group, using headphones and sharing through the chat box may help you express yourself more.
- You do not have permission to record the meeting or save the group chat.
- Keep your camera on while in sessions to foster cohesion and connectedness; it is fine to turn your camera off if you need to step away for a moment to limit distractions. Please remember to keep yourself muted when not speaking.
- Members can be helpful to each other by listening, showing understanding, and sharing what makes them feel comfortable. However, no one knows what is best for another person or what that person needs or wants to do; group members are welcome to provide support but not advice.
- All feelings are acceptable. Members are encouraged to express their feelings, understanding that members may express themselves differently. Sharing and talking open up more opportunities to gain support and insight from a group experience.

If specific behaviors continue to be concerning, facilitators may need to follow up individually with the member after that session ends to understand what was going on in that moment and use clinical judgment to assess the need for additional referrals.

The importance of being distraction-free is just as critical for the facilitator in shaping virtual group behavior. Paying attention to one's own on-screen behavior and managing your own environment models positive engagement skills for the group, much as you would if the group members were together in a room with you. Some of these guidelines may seem simple but they make a difference in helping your group members feel welcome and engaged:

- Turn off any phones in your vicinity and be sure your face and part of your upper torso are in the camera.
- Maintain eye contact with group members as best as you can, they can still notice when you are looking at them and attuned with them.

- Dress in a professional manner; if you would not wear it to work in person, don't wear it virtually.
- Make sure no one in your household (human or pet) will make a special guest appearance in your background.
- Whether you are conducting groups in your office or at home, make sure you are in a room that is quiet, that your lighting is adequate and welcoming, and that your background is as neutral as possible.

Pay special attention to objects that have the potential to be triggering for clients or may reveal more about you than is necessary. For instance, having pictures of you and your family in the background may engender strong reactions from grievers. Grieving parents may have a hard time seeing photos of you and your children in your background during such an intense time in their lives. As a facilitator you can address these reactions if they occur, but it is helpful to limit this exposure for clients as best as you can.

I have found several creative ways to utilize the virtual space in your favor as a facilitator. One way is to invite members to share objects or spaces in their home that are personally meaningful to them. Some members appreciate sharing photos of their special person who died or sacred altars they have created for reflection in their grief. Other members then gain ideas from this type of sharing on how to create spaces for themselves that helps them honor and remember their loved one. This "virtual show and tell" can also lead to rich discussion. Other activities can be modified for a virtual platform. For instance, a simple candle ceremony can still be accomplished by having everyone light and hold a candle in their own spaces as they take turns sharing part of a special poem or reading that the facilitator has chosen.

Many counselors have had to modify the way they support clients as they adjust to telehealth. Reading and assessing body language on a virtual platform can be challenging, especially when managing multiple "squares on a screen." Tears streaming down someone's face or a restless shaking in someone's leg is much easier to notice when they are in your presence. In a virtual platform, verbal cues take on much more importance.

One way to check on behaviors can be to ask, "Are those tears I notice every time you mention Judy's art?" or "It seems that as we talk about returning to the nursing home to pick up your mom's belongings, your hand starts to shake, is that right?" These observations can help gauge attunement to what clients may be experiencing and give clients an opportunity to confirm or correct these observations. In a group setting, it can be helpful to observe group members' reactions to each other and point it out as a way of creating cohesion in the group. For instance, you might say, "Christine, as you share about the intense loneliness you feel when you go to bed at night, I see several others nodding. Would anyone else like to share about their own experience of loneliness at night?" or "James, thanks for offering some suggestions to Kathy about how to navigate cleaning out Ben's desk at his office. Does anyone else have any other thoughts that might be helpful?" Facilitators may also need to shift how to convey empathy and compassion. Just as when offering face-to-face support, remind yourself that no singular approach will fit all clients in a virtual setting. Interventions need to be thoughtful, respectful, and open to client modification if they are to meet the needs of all your members. A direct gaze is hard to achieve in a virtual platform; reaching out a hand in support is not possible. This reality can be challenging for practitioners who are accustomed to using gentle touch as a show of empathy. As an alternative, reaching a hand to your heart is a visual that can carry a message of attunement to a special moment or heartbreaking emotion that a client is conveying. A gentle, "Yes, I hear you" or an attentive smile can communicate presence.

What about grieving children? How can we engage them in grief groups via a virtual platform? Regardless of age and development, some children can be hesitant to turn on their cameras. They may not want to show others the environment they live in, they may not feel comfortable with how they look on a screen, or they may feel that experiencing the up-close virtual view is a bit too intimate. For some tweens and teenagers, the virtual platform actually translates quite easily. In contrast, for younger children, a virtual platform can be quite challenging. Participation in virtual groups may also pose challenges for children and young adults with intellectual or developmental disabilities. Some barriers to participation may include needing a parent or guardian to help them get online; lack of privacy to communicate freely; more opportunities for distractions; and lack of ability to use group assistants to moderate behavior.

Working closely with parents and guardians to help them understand the importance of their child's participation, as well as how they can best assist in the process, can mitigate some of these challenges. Short tutorials with the parent or guardian and the child online together prior to joining a support group can help familiarize them with the process as well as provide an opportunity to review the group guidelines. Including parents and guardians in this process helps them become an essential support for the child and clarifies that they are important partners in making this experience enriching and meaningful. Here are some basic guidelines that can be helpful with children and teen groups:

- We all need to listen to one another and that will happen if one person is speaking at a time. You can raise your actual hand or raise your virtual hand when you want to speak. If you want to speak, but don't feel comfortable, you can use the chat.
- Your camera must be turned on and the group must see your face, just like they would if we were meeting in person.
- Please mute your microphone when you aren't talking.
- You do not have permission to record the meeting.
- Please try to find as private a space as you can; maybe it's your room, or the closet, or the bathroom. Using headphones or earbuds can give you some additional privacy.
- We know you might be using your parent's or guardian's phone or computer, but we hope you can use it during our entire time together. Of course, if there is an emergency, we understand.
- We won't have our tablecloths and markers, but if you can draw on paper at home, that might help. (It's nice for children to have the opportunity to doodle as it's hard to discuss challenging feelings).
- Also, snacks have been very important to our routine when we've met in person, right? It would be great to have a snack as a group when we meet. We might not all have chips and cookies nearby but see if you can find a snack to have with us.

Developing ongoing relationships with parents and guardians also allows you to more easily enlist their support if problems arise. For example, if a child continues to struggle for privacy and you hear constant distractions in the background, gently approaching the adults can be more helpful than putting the responsibility on the child. Adults are often not even aware that they or others in the home are interfering with their child's session. Realistically, some families may not have enough space in their home to appropriately limit distractions. You can work with the parent or guardian and the child to provide suggestions for solutions, such as headphones and using the chat box to allow the child to express themselves more privately than speaking out loud. These conversations with the family can also include a reminder about the group meeting schedule so that other members of the household can assist with minimizing distractions.

Just as with in-person groups, scheduling group times based on age and developmental need is important. While tweens and teens can generally still benefit from 90-minute or 2-hour online groups, younger children do better with one-hour virtual groups. Just as with adults, incorporating activities that foster connection among members can increase engagement. Activities should be short and engaging and, when appropriate, their spaces can be used as part of an activity. One such activity that works well is a virtual scavenger hunt. The facilitator gives children prompts such as, "Bring us an object that makes you feel powerful" or "Tell us about a space in your home that feels really comfortable to you."

Creative arts activities are still important ways to encourage grieving children to express themselves, but modifications are necessary for a virtual platform. Zoom offers a whiteboard feature that allows the meeting host to share a whiteboard that you and other participants can add to and everyone can see it in the virtual session. You can put a heading on the whiteboard that says, "Grief is…" and ask the children to write or draw their answers for everyone to see and discuss. Activities that require some movement keep children more engaged. Asking children to make a movement that shows how they feel in their grief can be fun while also teaching them the connection of their body with their thoughts and emotions.

Going forward, virtual groups will continue to change and evolve even after the pandemic is better controlled. Virtual platforms have many advantages and have allowed a broader range of grieving people to receive the help they need. Some of the groups that have greatly benefitted are older people who may not have the ability or desire to physically leave their home to attend in-person groups; individuals with a physical disability who may avoid in-person groups because of health concerns or transportation difficulties; individuals in rural areas who don't have access to in-person groups or individual therapists; grievers with young children who do not have childcare; and those caring for an ill family member who cannot leave their home for several hours at a time.

The delicate balance of maintaining the therapeutic frame through adhering to group guidelines while offering flexibility to accommodate for the challenges of virtual counseling is important. Clients are now faced with technological challenges layered on top of their emotional challenges and clinicians are tasked with stretching and repurposing their clinical skills to work in a virtual world. Clinicians will need to incorporate different self-care techniques and clients will need to adjust their expectations. As clinicians face a full workday spent looking at a computer screen, they will need to plan appropriate breaks to limit fatigue that can cause muscle weakness, back pain, and vision strain. Clients may need to allow themselves more time to practice utilizing a virtual platform and becoming comfortable with connecting with other grievers in this new way. Many grievers also enjoy continuing the conversation outside of group and many may long to meet for a cup of coffee in between sessions with other group members to share feelings and stories. These connections can happen less frequently or take longer to develop when meeting solely on a virtual platform.

Virtual groups have exponentially expanded the possibilities for grievers to receive care and support. For many, knowing that this option is available can be a relief as they try to juggle other responsibilities in their lives. For us as facilitators and clinicians, virtual groups create connection in ways we never really imagined we could provide. Our definition of community has broadened as we are now able to accept people outside the scope of their ability to participate in person. Creating online community support amongst group facilitators offers them opportunities to support one another, share resources, and network. Virtual groups have made their appearance in our time of great need and are here to stay as a source of support that we can readily call upon when barriers to in-person support remain.

Maria Georgopoulos, LMHC, FT, is Director of the Bereavement Services Department at Calvary Hospital. She is responsible for 32 bereavement support groups in the Bronx, Brooklyn, and Manhattan that serve hundreds of adults, children, and teenagers each year; leads a team of seven bereavement counselors; and spearheads Calvary's efforts to expand the Hospital's professional learning programs in the New York area. Prior to working at Calvary, Ms. Georgopoulos worked in the mental health profession in other settings, including The American Red Cross of Greater New York after 9/11. In addition to her work in bereavement, Ms. Georgopoulos is a licensed mental health counselor with a private practice in New York City and provides counseling for diverse populations of people with varying difficulties.

CHAPTER 10

Voices
Finding Resilience and Hope Amidst the Pain of Grief

Maryrose Sonsini Cidoni

Reader, this is a heartbreaking tale, like millions of others experienced during the COVID-19 pandemic. Sometimes I am still in disbelief. Is my mother, Gloria Sonsini Cidoni, really dead? Sometimes I am so angry that she was not allowed a wake or a proper funeral, no traditional Italian service that she so much deserved. Sometimes I am filled with rage; my neck tenses and my body aches.

The last time I visited my mom was March 7, 2020. We ate in the dining area of her New York City area nursing home. We spoke about my father who had died there 3 years earlier. She was so supportive, always listening calmly; I was so proud to be her youngest daughter. We listened to Engelbert Humperdinck and Johnny Mathis that night; they were her favorite singers. I can remember our last intense hug. I can still feel her body and smell her unique scent. My love endures.

Gloria's mother (my grandmother), Micalina Sonsini, died when my mother was just 6 years old. My mother's life became extremely difficult; she was tossed from family to family and suffered from anxiety and depression. She often lacked financial support and recalled the many times she went hungry. Unable to attend high school, she instead worked as a seamstress in a sweatshop. I always felt so sorry for her and wished that her early life could have been easier.

Still, she persevered. Gloria was loved by many. She greeted everyone warmly and with sincerity. Her last birthday party was celebrated outdoors on August 25, 2019, surrounded by a huge group of grandchildren, great-grandchildren, and so many other loved ones who were in attendance. She sang along with us, glowing and full of life and gratitude. The hardships of her youth seemed to disappear.

In early March 2020, I called the staff at the nursing home and spoke with a healthcare worker there. My mother, I was told, had a low-grade fever, and they had treated her with acetaminophen. To my disappointment, they had no plans to test her for COVID-19 at that time. Around this same time, my sister informed me that the home had called her and told her that due to federal and state regulations, they had posted signs that no one other than staff was allowed to enter.

I lived in fear that my mother was going to contact COVID-19, or that perhaps the fever meant that she had already contracted the virus. Soon after the lockdown, the home stopped answering phone calls. I would call 15 times in a row. If someone did answer, they would tell me they were too busy and then hang up the phone. Were they overwhelmed? I trusted them with my mother's life, and I was worried.

When I made attempts to visit with my mother via Zoom and did not get a response from the staff, I really knew something was wrong. My sister, who was able to make contact, continued to be reassured that our mother was fine.

By April 3, I had a very strong premonition that prompted me to go to take pictures outside of the home. I felt that my mother was going to die. I said to myself, "Mommy, this is the last time I will know that you are still alive." It was a powerful moment; perhaps God sent me there that day.

Two days later I received a phone call from a nurse who told me, "I don't know what's wrong with Gloria; she has a fever of 104 degrees and is having trouble breathing." I directed them to take my mother to a specific hospital; my sister and I panicked.

Soon thereafter, I received a call from the doctor at the hospital who told me the terrible news that my mother could die very quickly, and we had to make some very difficult decisions. He said it appeared that she had COVID-19; they were waiting for the test results. He said he did not want to intubate her because her organs could shut down, but he advised us to allow them to give her morphine with another mixture of medication to ease her discomfort. My sister and I quickly agreed with the doctor. As I hung up, my body shook, and I began to cry uncontrollably. This was going to be it.

A few hours later, the doctor on call made it possible for me to FaceTime with my mother. I saw her with the oxygen mask over her face. Her lips were turning blue and her head was turned to one side. I yelled out to her, "Mom, I love you," over and over again. "If I could,

I would be there, holding you and loving you." Being a trained opera singer, my voice can be very loud. The doctor said that she began moving her arms because she heard me. Soon after, she opened her large, deep brown, expressive eyes. She saw me, and I saw her sending me her love. I then sang Shubert's *Ave Maria* to her. She listened intently, then closed her eyes, and the doctor said she was once again unconscious. This was the last time I saw her alive. As I write this, I hang my head with respect and mourning.

Over the next few days my family and I prayed that she would pull through, since she continued to live a few days, and my niece had heard that others her age had fought it off. Unable to sleep one night because of this living nightmare, I heard my mother's voice telling me, "Mary, you are going to be able to take care of yourself." I pleaded with her: "Mom, oh Mom, don't tell me that!" We had lived together for many years, and we were so close to each other. Fifteen minutes later the hospital called and told me that she had just passed. In that moment, I never thought I would live through this.

Almost three weeks after April 8, which was the day she died, I was able to follow the hearse to the cemetery. Although my father had paid for her wake and ceremony, we could not see her because of the restrictions; we could not have a proper Catholic service and traditional wake. My mother Gloria did not deserve this.

Her coffin was a pearlized pink. Parked from a distance, I watched from inside my car. But how did I really know that it was her body in that coffin? During that time, many bodies were being stored for weeks before burial. I now go back to the cemetery often. I touch her name on the stone to feel her name engraved; when I look at it, though, her name gets cloudy and comes in and out of focus.

The experience of my mother's death from COVID-19 has had a profound impact on me. It took me months to leave the house. I became fearful of everything; I felt unable to function and lost trust in the world around me. I became afraid to touch anything because I was afraid of contracting COVID-19 myself. I would check over and over again if I had enough masks, gloves, hand sanitizers, alcohol sprays, paper towels. I panicked whenever I would see a person wearing a mask incorrectly or not wearing one at all. I would hold my breath when I passed people.

Since my mother's death I have been mostly alone, living in my parents' apartment. The loneliness can feel unbearable at times. Within the community of my mother's nursing home, I had become close to many of the other residents. I turned to some of them for trusted advice. Many of them were part of our holiday celebrations or birthday parties, including my mom's last big party with our family. Too many of these special people also died of COVID-19 around the same time as my mother. Sometimes it feels like I'm mourning a community of souls.

Sometimes I have found myself screaming in front of the church, howling "I hate you, God." I made calls to therapists; I made calls to a suicide helpline. I was informed by my employee assistance program about a support group at Calvary Hospital for people whose parents had died due to COVID-19. I am grateful to have had the opportunity to attend this group. Maria Georgopoulos, the director of bereavement services there, has been so helpful in leading me through this very difficult process of grief. She is amazingly comforting, warmhearted, and understanding; the other group members have also been so important to me. Maria is leading me through this very difficult process, along with my group members. I trust them and feel that I have a great deal of empathy with them, so I am not alone.

During this pandemic, I have been working remotely. I had to learn to teach on Google Classroom; it has been difficult, but many people have helped me. Yet I get very little response from my high school students when I am teaching music remotely. Most do not turn on their cameras or write in the chat, and they are only identified by one initial. It is sometimes a very lonely process, but I have learned to survive this by calling it my "radio show," in which I am the host. Having this routine has helped me, even though it is so removed from my usual interactive classes. I know that my students are just teenagers, and that they are suffering from trauma and depression because of the pandemic as well. By taking them on musical journeys, I want them to have fun and hope, and I tell them often that when we are back in the school building that I hope they will stop by my room so we can connect in person.

Despite my pain and loss, I now can acknowledge my resilience. I've been meditating, connecting with others, and singing, and these actions have given me hope for myself and my students. It has not been easy, but I am surviving, perhaps even growing. I would advise anyone who is going through a death of a loved one due to COVID-19 to reach out and seek help. There is support out there; you are not alone.

Maryrose Sonsini Cidoni *is a music teacher in the New York city schools and a professionally trained opera singer. Her mother, Gloria Sonsini Cidoni, died of COVID-19 on April 8, 2020.*

CHAPTER 11

Spiritual Challenges and Responses to the COVID-19 Pandemic

Gary S. Fink

The COVID-19 pandemic is more than a healthcare emergency; it is an existential crisis. The pandemic has changed how we live, how we interact, and how we view our environment. COVID-19 has undermined the assumptive world of those who came to believe that their everyday routines are safe and secure. This chapter will explore spiritual challenges and issues that have arisen for patients, families, and spiritual caregivers due to the COVID-19 pandemic. We will explore the impact of COVID-19 on coping with dying and how we grieve. Finally, we will look ahead at areas for further study and action.

SPIRITUAL CHALLENGES AND ISSUES FOR PATIENTS

Spiritual Distress: A World Turned Upside Down

The sudden and unexpected threat of COVID-19 has become a major source of spiritual distress for patients and families. Spiritual distress encompasses existential angst and feelings of uncertainty, despair, hopelessness, isolation, and disconnection (Puchalski et al., 2020). The spread and impact of this disease evokes existential fears of vulnerability, isolation, sudden decline, suffering at the end of life, and dying alone. Patients coping with serious illness have experienced separation from family and spiritual community, as lockdowns in hospitals, nursing facilities, and senior living residences prevent those who are ill from receiving the comfort of companionship from loved ones and friends (Carey et al., 2020). Before the pandemic, patients and families were routinely welcomed to sit with loved ones as death approached. Bedside vigils of family members were common, and family members were often looking on when patients drew their last breath. Because of high risks of infection in facilities, family visitation has been severely restricted or banned completely. The pandemic has forced family members to remain on the outside looking in. Although connections with a spiritual community have been shown to benefit health and well-being (Chen et al., 2020), government-ordered prohibitions of large gatherings for worship and prayer have disrupted those spiritual lifelines.

Until more effective treatments are found, the trajectory from diagnosis to decline to death may be a matter of days or weeks for the most vulnerable. The use of mechanical respirators to treat acute symptoms may negate the possibility of a "good death" free of discomfort. Underserved populations, especially communities of color, experience another layer of existential distress, as systematic inequality, distributive injustice of healthcare resources, and limited access to care result in higher rates of infection, acute symptoms, and death.

God, Religion, and Personal Faith

COVID-19 may evoke crises of faith, even among the faithful. Geppert and Pies (2020) explore both positive and negative effects of spiritual orientation as people cope with life-threatening illness and death. Some embrace their faith more tightly as a source of comfort. The authors cite a sign on a truck declaring that "Jesus is my vaccine" to illustrate that faith sometimes trumps science as a source of hope (p. 15). However, when the "Jesus vaccine" fails to protect the faithful from infection, when faith is not sufficient to provide immunity, those who fall ill from COVID-19 may question their spiritual worth, viewing illness as a sign of spiritual defect (p. 15).

A thorough spiritual assessment conducted by hospice chaplains and other spiritual caregivers can give insight into how clients make sense of their circumstances and how they view the question "Where is God in this pandemic?" While some may view the COVID-19 pandemic as Divine judgment, others may perceive that the Divine dwells among the suffering, providing comfort and sacred connection. Some may see the pandemic as a test of faith, while others may view COVID-19 as part of a Divine plan that is beyond our limited understanding. Hospice chaplains do not provide definitive theological answers, but rather help clients find spiritual perspectives and connections that reduce distress and bring comfort, especially when coping with new existential challenges of illness and isolation.

Spiritual Interventions: Addressing Spiritual Challenges for Patients and Families

COVID-19 challenges spiritual caregivers to adjust religious practices to overcome quarantines and social distancing protocols when ministering to the dying. Chaplains who cannot visit patients at home often collaborate with family members or caregivers who serve as intermediaries for remote transitional rituals. For example, the National Association of Catholic Chaplains published a guide for traditional rituals and prayers that can be recited at a distance by a chaplain or family member if a priest is not available. In addition, the Vatican has decreed that a plenary indulgence, or a full pardon of sins, be granted to anyone for whom a priest cannot be present at the bedside to provide the anointing of the sick (National Association of Catholic Chaplains, 2020).

A variety of tools and activities can be utilized by patients and families to deal with isolation and spiritual distress caused by the COVID-19 pandemic. Ritual objects or religious artifacts that represent transcendent connections, such as rosary beads, a prayer mat, or Sabbath candlesticks, can help maintain a connection to the larger community or to one's higher power. Nonreligious transitional objects, such as pictures or mementos, can provide spiritual comfort by evoking transcendent connections with family.

Psychiatrists Harold Koenig and John Peteet suggest that spiritual connections are key to addressing existential anxiety associated with the pandemic. Spiritual activities may include regular worship or devotions, meditation, mindfulness, fostering hope, and aligning personal goals with core values. In addition, they recommend maintaining daily rhythms and activity, engaging with others and fostering compassion through support for particular people in need, attending to physical health, and finding or creating sources of joy and inspiration (Koenig, 2020; Peteet, 2020).

COVID-19 and Spiritual Communities

Kranz et al. (2020) point out that although religion can be a significant source of resilience, religiosity is a risk factor for poor health outcomes because it correlates with rejection of pandemic-related public health measures (e.g., wearing masks, social distancing, vaccines). Various religious groups in the United States and throughout the world have defiantly opposed government-ordered restrictions on public gatherings for worship and communal practices during pandemic peaks (Stueckelberger & Ciocan, 2020).

On the other hand, VanderWeele (2020) argues that the imperatives of love of God and love of neighbor require spiritual groups to suspend face-to-face contact during the pandemic to prevent the spread of COVID-19. This pandemic highlights the need for effective public health education, and for government leaders, scientists, and religious leaders across the spectrum to work together to overcome misinformation and distrust.

In the place of face-to-face meetings, multiple social media platforms have provided connection and communication for communities and families. Creating sacred space for virtual online worship services in homes has been an innovative response to social distancing and has led to a broad redefinition of sacred versus secular space. Places within homes have become holy altars as they are transformed into sacred spaces and linked with dozens or hundreds of similarly created temporary sanctuaries (Bryson et al., 2020).

Although virtual meetings can overcome social distance, many people do not have access to adequate broadband, computers, smartphones, or tablets, or they lack the skills to make the technology work. Spiritual communities can raise awareness of economic and generational factors that prevent underserved populations and older age groups from accessing tools for mitigating social isolation.

SPIRITUAL CHALLENGES AND ISSUES FOR PROFESSIONAL CAREGIVERS

Spiritual Care and the Interdisciplinary Team

Beginning in the spring of 2020, hospitals and care facilities routinely adopted COVID-19 lockdown protocols prohibiting staff chaplains and community-based spiritual caregivers from providing face-to-face visits in an effort to prioritize essential medical care. Hall (2020) argues for spiritual care providers to be allowed face-to-face visitation with hospital patients, in accordance with facility infection control protocols. Spiritual care is essential in addressing the human need for transcendence and connectedness, and to mitigate fear, pain, and isolation. In other words, spiritual care is essential care *because* COVID-19 restrictions exacerbate spiritual isolation and existential issues (Ferrell et al., 2020).

Delivery of Spiritual Care and Ministry of Virtual Presence

Hospice care has been transformed in a very short period because of the pandemic. Before COVID-19, the hospice team, including chaplains, provided robust face-to-face contact. Due to restrictions on in-person patient visits, spiritual care staffs quickly adopted emerging technology and new skills to provide telehealth support to patients and families. However, from the point of view of patient and family, the new world of remote spiritual support can feel less personal and more distant. Providing companionship for the dying, a core spiritual value of end-of-life care, has been constrained. Hospices have suspended programs to provide companionship to the dying, such as 11th Hour Volunteers, No One Dies Alone programs, and end-of-life doulas.

In the new reality of spiritual care, remote support replaced face-to-face support, "high-touch" spiritual care gave way to "no-touch" spiritual care, phone calls replaced house calls, and instead of offering ministry of presence, chaplains provide ministry of *virtual* presence. Consequently, hospices and spiritual care departments have established protocols that specify when virtual chaplain visits or face-to-face visits are most appropriate (Hawkins et al., 2020).

How do virtual visits impact the therapeutic process? Traditionally, the trust that is formed between client and counselor facilitates the healing process. An effective rapport facilitates positive transference, which can be a useful tool in validating clients' "essential selves," especially regarding confession and forgiveness (Bard, 2020, p. 81). The therapeutic relationship between spiritual counselor and client depends upon the creation of a safe space for trust-building, self-disclosure, and spiritual healing. During the pandemic, safe space is often virtual (Sprik et al., 2020), created in telephone calls with a reassuring voice and in video calls with voice, eye contact, facial gestures, and a calming background.

Initial evidence indicates that virtual and video chat technology with tablets, computers, or smartphones can be an effective way of providing pastoral care while social distancing (Byrne & Nuzum, 2020). Dominikus (2020) concludes that online counseling has been shown to be effective for a number of issues, including depression, panic disorder, social anxiety, posttraumatic stress disorder (PTSD), and eating disorders.

Virtual ministry challenges spiritual counselors to adopt a new role and skill set (Bryson et al., 2020). A colleague of this writer recently remarked, "Now I'm working as pastor *and* producer!" Counselors now need to be aware of production values including lighting, sound, background, appearance, set decoration, and eye contact with the camera. A potential benefit of this new role is the enhancement of clinical skills through increased attention to visual cues, gestures, therapeutic environment, and attentive listening.

Impact of COVID-19 on Religious Communities

Spiritual leaders and faith-based institutions have responded to lockdown measures and social distancing rules by promoting online worship services, which has led to a broad redefinition of sacred vs. secular space. Bryson et al. (2020) point to thousands of newly created sacred spaces but cautions that "blurring the lines between sacred and secular spaces risks desacralising more than sanctifying, as new online delivery models make different demands on clergy and risks the development of churches more centered on celebrity and charisma than on theology" (p. 370). On the other hand, he notes that virtual online services allow for unprecedented expansion of congregational geographical boundaries and enhance inclusion of infirm congregants and shut-ins.

During periods of high COVID-19 transmission, limitations on social gatherings have forced spiritual communities and religious leaders to modify traditional rituals and create new ones. To avoid large gatherings, some churches sponsored "drive-through" communion. Others provided "ashes to go" on Ash Wednesday for pickup. From Saudi Arabia to Egypt to the United States, Muslim leaders allowed Friday prayers to be recited at home rather than gathering at the mosque in order to preserve public health (Hubbard, 2020). Easter and Passover observances were significantly curtailed in 2020. The Hindu Holi festival in March and the Sikh festival of Vaisakhi in April faced severe restrictions (Stueckelberger & Ciocan, 2020). Synagogues, churches, mosques, and temples routinely began online streaming of Sabbath, life cycle, and other religious services to avoid face-to-face contact.

Remote Spiritual Interventions

Narrative therapies are useful tools in addressing existential questions and are compatible with remote spiritual care by telephone or video chat. The "ultimate" questions often raised by patients and family members include: *What is the meaning of my life? What meaning is there in my death? What is my place and purpose in the universe? Where will I find comfort for my fears?*

Narrative approaches including reminiscence, life review, dignity therapy, and legacy letters can be powerful tools to help patients find or make meaning in their lives (Fink, 2011). Narrative interventions can help to validate and affirm the value of a person's life and legacy. The dying person may process unresolved issues and reframe a personal narrative to find greater peace. At the same time, clinicians must recognize the risks of evoking negative or painful recollections if there is not enough time, energy, or ability to process memories in a positive way due to remote communication or rapid patient decline.

Other interventions that are consistent with remote spiritual care include prayer or scripture to enhance spiritual connection; visualizations or meditation to address anxiety and isolation; pastoral counseling to address spiritual issues; using music to foster calm or trigger helpful emotions; normalizing spiritual questions and anxieties; facilitating spiritual connection with a higher power or nature; and fostering continuing bonds with people, living or dead, whose relationship with the client brings comfort.

Spiritual Support for Non-COVID-19 Patients

Mandatory social distancing places burdens on individuals with illnesses other than COVID-19, especially those in healthcare facilities. Feelings of spiritual isolation and abandonment may be magnified by lockdowns and social distancing protocols; and patients with cognitive impairment may lack understanding of the COVID-19 restrictions (Drummond & Carey, 2020). Drummond and Carey point to the importance of familiar spiritual interventions for the frail elderly in facilities because "when the world becomes shrunken to the size of the facility, the transcendent becomes an even more important filter and interpretive framework" (p. 19).

Spiritual caregivers can remotely support minimally responsive or nonresponsive patients in several ways, especially those who live at home with a caregiver. A chaplain can send prerecorded music, hymns, prayers, or blessings to the caregiver's phone to be played at the bedside. A chaplain can arrange a conference call with dispersed family members through the caregiver's phone at the bedside during which the chaplain might offer prayers, blessings, or words of affirmation that will be heard at the bedside and by the family.

Burnout, Ethical Issues, and Self-Care

Spiritual caregivers experience existential distress when they are overwhelmed, feel helpless to adequately alleviate spiritual pain, or have difficulty making sense of suffering. In July of 2020, the *Economist* reported that a Catholic priest administered the last rites at more than five times the usual rate while also providing appropriate final blessings for hospital patients of other faiths. During the initial surge of pandemic deaths, the *New York Times* reporter Emma Goldberg (2020) noted that "chaplains are carrying more of their own grief and fear. Many worry about being infected with the virus and bringing it home to their families."

Greene et al. (2020) suggest that stressors caused by the pandemic may result in burnout, moral injury, and secondary trauma for spiritual caregivers, and offer the following actions as protective: Acknowledgment of moral conflicts, maintaining a sense of purpose, spiritual engagement, supervisory and peer support, social support, self-care, and professional counseling support.

Hospice chaplains are especially susceptible to moral injury when involved in ethical issues and decision making. If resources or staffing are inadequate to handle a surge in COVID-19 patients, how will decisions be made regarding who is admitted for hospice care? How will healthcare organizations ensure equitable access to limited resources, including for underserved communities? Parker and Mirzaali (2020) caution that "unavoidable moral failure" could result from a forced choice between individual needs and the greater good.

Other ethical issues raised by COVID-19 include timely and fully informed consent, pediatric patient needs, resources for non-COVID-19 patients, moral distress of staff, legal liabilities and financial considerations, community participation in institutional decision making, and mitigation of structural inequities and discrimination (McGuire et al., 2020).

The coronavirus pandemic heightens the need for professional caregivers to embrace spiritual, emotional, and physical practices of self-care such as blessings and prayers recited upon hand washing, meditative and devotional time, fostering denominational contacts, religious music and traditional chants, connection with nature, regular exercise, and peer support.

Inclusive Spiritual Care

The disproportionate impact of the pandemic on low-income groups and underserved communities highlights the need to focus attention on communities most affected by COVID-19. Culturally sensitive programs have emerged that serve as models of inclusive spiritual care for underserved communities. Examples of innovative projects that have been developed to address spiritual needs of underserved communities include:

- Project Trust, a 3-year-old program in the San Francisco Bay Area, developed a series of short videos, disseminated through local churches, to promote trust between the African American community, local pastors, and public health experts (Thompkins et al., 2020).
- A new approach in the field of social work utilizes spiritual-based practices and the Critical Race Theory method of counterstorytelling to mitigate loneliness and stress among socially isolated older African American adults (Adams & Tyson, 2020).
- Indigenous people in Canada use cultural and spiritual symbols that evoke prayer and healing to help their community cope with the COVID-19 crisis (Banning, 2020).

IMPACT OF COVID-19 ON FUNERAL RITUALS AND BEREAVEMENT

All faiths and cultures have funeral and mourning rituals which provide psychological benefits, including structuring ways to process grief, facilitating emotional expression and social support, confirming the reality of death, and sharing memories that crystallize continuing bonds. Funeral rituals also provide strong spiritual benefits including fostering transcendent connections and helping survivors make sense of the loss.

Pandemic-related restrictions complicate the grieving process. Funeral rituals limited by social distance protocols prevent mourners from receiving expressions of physical support through touch or physical presence. Mourners might not be able to touch or carry the coffin, participate in the funeral service, or gather together after the formal service has ended (Murphy, 2020). Certain rituals have been suspended or modified. For instance, Muslim and Jewish traditions prescribe ritual washing and shrouding of a body. In some communities, those practices have been modified to include personal protective equipment (PPE) and other COVID-19 protocols, while others suspended the practice because of shortages of PPE and other public health concerns. In addition, the world-wide attention to COVID-19 has led to feelings of disenfranchised grief (Doka, 1999) among mourners whose loved ones died from other causes.

Technology is being utilized to virtually bring people together for funerals and bereavement support across the religious spectrum (Schuck et al., 2020). Counselors, clergy, funeral directors, families, and faith communities have developed a variety of accommodations and adjustments to traditional bereavement practices, including:

- video streaming of funeral services and burials with restricted attendance;
- video streaming of prayers preceding a cremation;
- virtual memorial gatherings from homes of participants;
- prerecorded remembrances from people who cannot attend a virtual gathering;
- online guest books and Facebook pages for condolences and remembrances;
- congregations recognizing recent deaths and mourners during virtual or livestreamed worship services;
- congregations creating special services to recognize recent deaths and mourners;
- video recordings of funerals, burials, and virtual memorial gatherings for those who could not attend; and
- creative memorial activities using photos, art, music, or writing for personal comfort or to share with others.

At this writing, there appears to be mixed reaction to the promulgation of new or modified bereavement activities and rituals (Burrell & Selman, 2020). Some mourners lament the loss of face-to-face social contact and report feeling a lack of closure when traditional practices and gatherings cannot be held. Others, however, report a sense of relief at simplified arrangements and intimate gatherings. Some mourners find virtual gatherings too distant and impersonal, yet others are comforted that people from around the world can attend a virtual memorial service.

Unanticipated consequences have emerged from virtual ritual. Wood (2020) reports that through video streaming technology,

Muslim women witness and feel present at burials, which they traditionally do not attend. In Jewish tradition, the need to video stream shiva (bereavement) worship services on Zoom has expanded the definition of a "minyan," a prayer quorum. Some pastors report that attendance at funerals is much greater on Zoom than in person.

Burrell and Selman (2020) reviewed emerging literature regarding the beneficial versus detrimental impact of modified bereavement rituals. The results were inconclusive, but two important findings merit mentioning. The authors assert that function outweighs form, as "restrictions to funeral practices do not necessarily entail poor outcomes or experiences for the bereaved: it is not the number of attendees or even the type of funeral which determines how supportive it is, but rather how meaningful the occasion is, and how connected it helps mourners feel" (p. 32). Secondly, they state that "a sense of control was a key determinant of whether participants identified funeral practices and rituals as helpful or unhelpful" (p. 34). These findings are consistent with the anxiety, uncertainty, and lack of control experienced during the COVID-19 pandemic.

LOOKING AHEAD

A number of questions need to be further explored to gain a greater appreciation for the impact of changing models of spiritual care and to learn best practices to address the spiritual challenges that have emerged from the encounter with COVID-19.

- What are the benefits and burdens of remote pastoral care versus in-person support for the patient and for the professional caregiver?
- What tools will allow us to measure the efficacy of virtual visits versus face-to-face visits?
- What assessment tools will help identify a need for face-to-face visits versus remote support?
- How will productivity concerns, medical models, and financial pressures drive hospices and other healthcare organizations toward remote spiritual care?
- How will regulatory changes impact remote spiritual care?
- How will the impact of COVID-19 on rituals and responses to grief and loss affect the bereavement process?

- What strategies effectively address opposition within faith groups to public health measures and foster partnerships between scientists, government, and religious communities?

The COVID-19 pandemic has significantly impacted spirituality and the practice of spiritual care. Religious beliefs may continue to evolve as individuals and groups continue to discern or interpret the meaning of the COVID-19 pandemic through spiritual perspectives. Clinicians may continue to seek ways to provide efficient and effective spiritual support through telehealth, in addition to face-to-face visits. Time will tell how the effects of COVID-19 will linger.

May all who have experienced traumatic life disruption and loss find resilience and peace in the days to come.

Gary S. Fink, DMin, is Senior Vice President of Counseling and Family Support at Montgomery Hospice in Rockville, MD, where he supports the counseling departments, directs the Spiritual Counseling staff, and leads interfaith community outreach efforts. He served as a congregational rabbi for more than 25 years, retiring from the pulpit to establish a pastoral counseling practice specializing in grief, life-limiting illness, and end-of-life issues. Rabbi Fink was ordained at Hebrew Union College in Cincinnati and earned a doctorate at Howard University Divinity School, concentrating in end-of-life care. He holds a Graduate Certificate in Thanatology. Rabbi Fink was selected as a panelist for the 2011 Hospice Foundation of America's (HFA) Living with Grief® program focusing on Spirituality and End-of-Life Care and authored a chapter in the accompanying textbook. Since then, he has served as a panelist for a variety of programs sponsored by HFA.

References

Adams, R., & Tyson, C. (2020). "There is a Balm in Gilead:" Black social workers' spiritual counterstory on the COVID-19 crisis. *Social Work in Public Health*. Retrieved on September 5, 2020, from https://doi.org/10.1080/19371918.2020.1806169

Banning, J. (July 6, 2020). How Indigenous people are coping with COVID-19. *CMAJ, 192*(27), e787-788.

Bard, T. (2020). COVID-19 and a new normal? *Journal of Pastoral Care & Counseling, 74*(2), 81.

Bryson, J., Andres, L., & Davies, A. (2020). COVID-19, virtual church services and a new temporary geography of home. *Royal Dutch Geographical Society, 111*(3), 360-372.

Burrell, A., & Selman, L. (2020). How do funeral practices impact bereaved relatives' mental health, grief and bereavement? A mixed methods review with implications for COVID-19. *OMEGA—Journal of Death and Dying, 0*(0), 1-39. Retrieved on September 4, 2020 from https://journals.sagepub.com/doi/pdf/10.1177/0030222820941296

Byrne, M., & Nuzum, D. (2020). Pastoral closeness in physical distancing: The use of technology in pastoral ministry during COVID-19. *Health and Social Care Chaplaincy, 8*(2).

Carey, L., Swift, C., & Burton, M. (2020). COVID-19: Multinational perspectives of providing chaplaincy, pastoral, and spiritual care. *Health and Social Care Chaplaincy, 8*(2), 133-142.

Chen, Y., Kim, E. S., & VanderWeele, T. J. (2020). Religious-service attendance and subsequent health and well-being throughout adulthood: Evidence from three prospective cohorts. *International Journal of Epidemiology*. Retrieved on September 4, 2020, from https://doi.org/10.1093/ije/dyaa120

Civil Rites. (July 11, 2020). As few Americans go to church, chaplains are finding work elsewhere. *The Economist*, (436)20.

Doka, K. J. (1999). Disenfranchised grief. *Bereavement Care, 18*(3), 37-39.

Dominikus, D. B. S., (2020). Online/cyber counseling services in the COVID-19 outbreak: Are they really new? *Journal of Pastoral Care & Counseling, 74*(3), 166–174.

Drummond, D., & Carey, L. (2020). Chaplaincy and spiritual care response to COVID-19: An Australian case study – The McKellar Centre. *Health and Social Care Chaplaincy, 8*(2).

Ferrell, B., Handzo, G., Picchi, T., Puchalski, C., & Rosa, W. (2020). The urgency of spiritual Care: COVID-19 and the critical need for whole-person palliation. *Journal of Pain and Symptom Management, 60*(3), e7-11.

Fink, G. (2011). Legacy and spirituality at the end of life. In K. J. Doka & A. S. Tucci (Eds.), *Spirituality and End-of-Life Care*, pp. 73-85. Washington, DC: Hospice Foundation of America.

Geppert, C., & Pies, R. (2020). The upside and downside of religion, spirituality, and health. *Psychiatric Times, 37*(7), 1.

Goldberg, E. (April 11, 2020). Hospital chaplains try to keep the faith during the coronavirus pandemic. *The New York Times*. Retrieved on September 5, 2020 from https://www.nytimes.com/2020/04/11/health/coronavirus-chaplains-hospitals.html

Greene, T., Bloomfield, M., & Billings, J. (2020). Psychological trauma and moral injury in religious leaders during COVID-19. *Psychological Trauma: Theory, Research, Practice, and Policy, 12*(S1), S143-S145.

Hall, D. (2020). We can do better: Why pastoral care visitation to hospitals is essential, especially in times of crisis. *Journal of Religion and Health, 59*, 2283-2287.

Hawkins, J. P., Gannon, C., & Palfrey, J., (2020). Virtual visits in palliative care: About time or against the grain? *BMJ Supportive & Palliative Care, 10*, 331-336.

Hubbard, B. (April 25, 2020). A Ramadan like no other: Images from around the world. *The New York Times*. Retrieved on September 4, 2020 from https://www.nytimes.com/2020/04/25/world/ramadan-photos.html?action=click&module=Top+ Stories&pgtype= Homepage&fbclid=IwAR2JkSbfm4YqPaHqND23S7Iep3vCUi my4WuqhIu4PFP3aPSvQFKfHmmwbPY

Koenig, H. (2020). Maintaining health and well-being by putting faith into action during the COVID-19 pandemic. *Journal of Religion and Health, 59*, 2205-2214.

Kranz, D., Niepel, C., Botes, E., & Greiff, S. (September 24, 2020). Religiosity predicts unreasonable coping with COVID-19. *Psychology of Religion and Spirituality*. Advance online publication. http://dx.doi.org/10.1037/rel0000395

McGuire, A., Aulisio, M., Davis, F. D., Erwin, C., Harter, T. D., Jagsi, R.,...The COVID-19 Task Force of the Association of Bioethics Program Directors (ABPD). (2020). Ethical challenges arising in the COVID-19 pandemic: An overview from the Association of Bioethics Program Directors (ABPD) Task Force. *The American Journal of Bioethics*, *20*(7), 15-27.

Murphy, K. (2020). Death and grieving in a changing landscape: Facing the death of a loved one and experiencing grief during COVID-19. *Health and Social Care Chaplaincy*, *8*(2).

National Association of Catholic Chaplains. (2020). Questions and answers regarding sacramental practice during the COVID-19 pandemic. Retrieved on April 28, 2020 from https://www.nacc.org/wp-content/uploads/2020/03/QA-regarding-sacramental-practice-during-the-COVID-3.31.20.pdf

Parker, J., & Mirzaali, M. (March 16, 2020). The moral cost of coronavirus. *Journal of Medical Ethics*. Retrieved on September 5, 2020 from https://blogs.bmj.com/medical-ethics/2020/03/16/the-moral-cost-of-coronavirus/

Peteet, J. (2020). COVID-19 anxiety. *Journal of Religion and Health*, *59*, 2203–2204.

Puchalski, C., Bauer, R., Ferrell, B., Abu-Shamsieh, K., Chan, N., Delgado-Guay, M., ...Vandenhoeck, A. (2020). Palliative care in the COVID-19 pandemic. Briefing note: Interprofessional spiritual care in the time of COVID-19. *International Association for Hospice & Palliative Care*. Retrieved on September 4, 2020 from http://globalpalliativecare.org/covid-19/uploads/briefing-notes/briefing-note-interprofessional-spiritual-care-in-the-time-of-covid-19.pdf

Schuck, D., Hens-Piazza, G., & Sadler, R. (June 1, 2020). Different faiths, same pain: How to grieve a death in the coronavirus pandemic. *The Conversation*. Retrieved on September 4, 2020 from https://theconversation.com/different-faiths-same-pain-how-to-grieve-a-death-in-the-coronavirus-pandemic-138185

Sprik, P., Keenan, A. J., Bosell, D., Cheeseboro, S., Meadors, P., & Grossoehme, D. (2020). Feasibility and acceptability of a telephone-based chaplaincy intervention in a large, outpatient oncology center. *Supportive Care in Cancer*, *10*, 1007.

Stueckelberger, C., & Ciocan, C. (2020). Religious controversies in COVID-19. *Dialogo*, 6(2), 168-185.

Thompkins, F., Goldblum, P., Lai, T., Hansell, T., Barclay, A., & Brown, L. M. (2020). A culturally specific mental health and spirituality approach for African Americans facing the COVID-19 pandemic. *Psychological Trauma: Theory, Research, Practice, and Policy*, 12(5), 455-456.

VanderWeele, T. (2020). Love of neighbor during a pandemic: Navigating the competing goods of religious gatherings and physical health. *Journal of Religion and Health*, 59, 2196-2202.

Wood, P. (April 20, 2020). Lockdown-era Zoom funerals are upending religion traditions—and they may change the way we grieve forever. *Prospect*. Retrieved on September 5, 2020 from https://www.prospectmagazine.co.uk/philosophy/funerals-during-lockdown-coronavirus-covid-religious-tradition-zoom-grief

CHAPTER 12

Voices
Our Buildings are Closed,
but Our Churches are Open

Paul A. Metzler

I am a semiretired Episcopal priest, psychotherapist, and grief specialist living in St. Louis, Missouri. My experience of how one denomination responded to the coronavirus pandemic has been lived within the ecclesiastical structure of the Episcopal Diocese of Missouri. This diocese covers the eastern half of the state, which includes 42 congregations and additional centers of ministry, such as university campus chaplaincies, chaplaincy to juvenile detention centers, an Episcopal Service Corps residence, and multiple food pantry and feeding ministries throughout the diocese. My diocese is a part of The Episcopal Church (TEC) with dioceses across the United States and beyond. TEC is a member of the worldwide Anglican Communion, an ecclesiastical family of churches in more than 165 countries in communion with the Archbishop of Canterbury.

All of these dioceses and churches have been touched by COVID-19, but I have struggled along with other clergy here in the Diocese of Missouri to faithfully maintain the essential functions of the churches while protecting the health of the public as well as our members.

DIOCESAN AND NATIONAL CHURCH RESPONSE TO SUSPEND PUBLIC WORSHIP

As the pandemic unfolded with full fury in the state of Missouri, the diocese and its congregations quickly took preventive steps regarding worship gatherings to protect our church community and the broader community from virus transmission. A central tenet in Christian theology is Jesus' teaching to "Love the Lord your God with all your heart, with all your soul, and with all your mind. This is the greatest and most important commandment. The second is like it, Love your neighbor as yourself" (Matthew 22:37-39, NRSV, 1989). Equating the love of God and the love of neighbor shapes much of the spirituality of the Episcopal Church. This centrality of "the way of love" helped our leadership at all levels respond wisely and rapidly to the crisis.

As early as March 4, 2020, our Bishop's Office issued a statement, *Responding to the Coronavirus*, to review the best public health information and church resources known at that time. The statement detailed action steps for clergy and congregations to diminish the spread of the virus even while maintaining public worship, including the weekly celebration of the Holy Eucharist and reception of Holy Communion each Sunday.

The Bishop's statement went on to affirm that the Church is often at its best when responding to a natural disaster or tragedy of any kind. Our community-based faith congregations were encouraged to mobilize in love and care for their neighbors as well as themselves as the pandemic unfolded. Soon thereafter, our Presiding Bishop encouraged Episcopal Church members and all people across the nation to wear a mask in love and protection for others, even while Missouri Governor Michael Parsons was reluctant to issue statewide orders to mitigate the spread, such as mandatory mask wearing or limitations on public gatherings.

By March 16, 2020, the two bishops overseeing the Diocese, working in close cooperation and following the guidance of the Centers for Disease Control and Prevention (CDC) and the World Health Organization, directed that public worship be suspended in an effort to slow the spread of COVID-19. This difficult but necessary response caused a great deal of stress for church leaders and, of course, for congregants and others who needed spiritual guidance and attention during this crisis.

The decision to suspend public worship and refrain from in-person ministry of any kind had significant impact on what are considered routine activities of a priest within the life of a congregation. We could no longer administer sacramental rites such as baptism, weddings, anointing of the dying, public funerals, or the burial of the dead as we were accustomed. Deacons and priests found it difficult to offer pastoral support or spiritual direction, as most in-person activities were either suspended altogether or dramatically altered as ecclesiastical authorities applied the rapidly emerging CDC guidelines for safe practice. The apprehension and losses for church leaders were compelling and compounding.

Not since the 1918 influenza pandemic, commonly but erroneously named the Spanish flu, had the diocese been impacted by such a widespread health crisis. Public health authorities at that time had issued orders against public gatherings, which included closing churches. In response, the then Bishop Frederick Foote Johnson wrote that "the attitude generally has been one of protesting compliance" (*The Church News*, 1918) as the populace came to terms with the epidemic but questioned whether public health authorities had the right to order restrictions on public gatherings.

During the current pandemic, the concerns went further than public gatherings and church services. Many hospital and healthcare systems have found it necessary to prevent clergy from entering to offer prayers and anointing to the sick and dying. This difficult but reasonable restriction has created deep anguish for clergy, parishes, and families, leading to such heartbreaking realities as last rites offered via a cell phone held to a patient's ear by a compassionate healthcare professional inside while clergy and families remained outside, unable to be together at the profound moment of the death of a loved one. I know a priest who became a front-porch-pastoral-visitor expert as she prayed outside in front of closed storm doors or picture windows, speaking loud enough to be heard.

Supporting Clergy

Recognizing that many clergy felt disempowered and purposeless from the many restrictions on their roles, our diocese leadership initiated a weekly Clergy Zoom Conference in late March. Designed to support the health and well-being of the ordained clergy, each of the meetings included prayer and scripture, sharing via chat rooms, updates on public healthcare guidelines, and educational presentations to enable clergy to function wisely and effectively in a time of great turmoil and loss. For many clergy, their education about grief and loss was insufficient or outdated, or both.

I was asked to offer a presentation on contemporary understandings of grief, loss, and bereavement to update the knowledge and skills of clergy as they ministered to the sick and dying, as well as to their families, in the midst of the crisis. As part of this educational process, I prepared a resource document, *Considerations for Clergy Ministering to the Sick, At the Time of Death, and The Burial of the Dead in the Age of COVID-19* (Diocese of Missouri, 2020).

This document focused first on self-care, both spiritual and physical, as the crucial building block upon which all professional ministries must be based. Additionally, my presentation included strategies for:

- establishing interpersonal connection and presence during the pandemic despite the limitations of physical spacing;
- processing grief from nondeath losses, including shattered assumptions, ambiguous or disenfranchised losses, and the depletion that compounding multiples losses can cause;
- recognizing the importance of establishing continued bonds and meaning making in the grief that follows a death;
- understanding the trajectory of grief and the many indicators that lead to complicated grief responses;
- appreciating the stealth role of blame, shame, and guilt in the grief losses of a pandemic; and
- planning for how to minister at a death; preplanning with local funeral directors for the logistics of conducting an outdoor, safely spaced funeral with limited attendance; and prescheduling future individual or group memorial services for when a parish can open its building again.

The goal of this information was to help reduce anxiety and facilitate adaptation as clergy absorbed such totally new ways to "do church." The Clergy Zoom Conferences on other relevant topics continued throughout 2020 and our bishop maintained this vibrant connection among the clergy on a bi-weekly basis. One might say that it was an unexpected blessing from the COVID-19 crisis that our clergy have had more frequent and better-attended "face-to-face" communication and education programs than ever before.

Adaptations

Our clergy and congregations were compelled by these circumstances to immediately learn how to offer online worship via Facebook, Zoom, YouTube, Vimeo, and other livestream resources. For most congregations, this transition was unanticipated. Local parishes were unprepared with appropriate equipment or expertise for broadcasting worship services. Priests and deacons experienced a sudden, steep learning curve as the electronic church was birthed essentially overnight in our diocese. However, some churches did conduct occasional stay-in-your-car parking lot worship services to enable a greater sense of being physically together.

Many parishioners, especially older parishioners, needed personal tutorials on how to "Zoom-to-Church" on a Sunday morning or participate in worship via YouTube. Instruction on how to mute and stay muted became quite comically crucial for conducting online worship. Adapting to electronic methods of giving donations or continuing pledges was also vital, as most congregations experienced significant financial decline.

At the same time, many clergy also rediscovered how much could be accomplished with pastoral phone calls to offer support and prayer, especially before a surgery or other significant event. Others found that conducting the Rite of Spiritual Communion online or over the phone could still have great meaning. These acts of pastoral care were often further extended with follow-up notes and prayers mailed to parishioners. Some congregations also delivered packages for home worship, Advent wreaths, Christmas poinsettias, and other offerings to keep the church "open" even while the building was closed.

Personal Reactions

The emerging reality of COVID-19 worried me deeply, as my wife and I are in the at-risk, older, with preexisting conditions, category. We started our own personal stay-at-home orders and used face masks and hand sanitizers if we did go out for necessities. Yet, many in our region and state expressed dismissive attitudes about the efficacy of stay-at-home orders, the importance of social distancing, or the use of face masks. Governor Parsons, like President Donald Trump, nearly always appeared in public without a mask. At a later time in the continuing crisis, he stated: "You don't need government to tell you to wear a dang mask. If you want to wear a dang mask, wear a mask" (Huguelet, 2020).

The surreal nature of the obstinate refusal of so many to take the known science of the virus spread seriously inspired me to take liberties with a well-known prayer poem, *Christ Has No Body But Yours Now*, attributed to St. Teresa of Avila, a 16th century spiritual writer.

Coronavirus-19 Has No Body But Yours

Coronavirus-19 has no body now but yours

No hands, no feet on earth but yours.

Yours are the eyes with which it sees the world to taint

Yours are the feet on which it spreads through the earth.

Yours the hands with which it touches to contaminate

Yours the viral breath that fills the air between us

Yours are the hands, the eyes, the feet, the breath that brings CV-19 to

home, to the workplace, to a holy place,

to the eating or the playing place.

Coronavirus-19 has no power to spread and survive

without you and your body.

*   *   *   *   *

Yet in that body God graces a brain

Yours to use to think and to learn

Yours to perceive the world in love

Yours the brain to comprehend and restrain

Until again God's creation fully alive

Is safely embraced by all.

My amateur effort to use St. Teresa's prayer to satirize the careless behaviors of those who came to be known as the "anti-maskers" seemed to resonate with others when it was published in the weekly diocesan e-newsletter. Many of us were alarmed that while we strived to minimize the spread of the virus, many others seemed to fail to understand the fundamentals of the viral spread.

FINDING WAYS TO REMAIN FAITHFUL

I often use the term *sacred sadness* to acknowledge that grief brings us the most fundamental meanings and purposes of our lives. The grief of losing our accustomed ways of worship, education, pastoral care, mutual support, and institutional function was real and brought a very human sadness. This grief is, of course, compounded by the profound sorrow of the deaths of many parishioners. Yet finding ways to remain faithful and discovering that all that was essential was still accessible by new means brought real joy to my colleagues and community of faith. While we do not know what church will look like post-pandemic, we know that, like everything else in the world, it will be different. My hope is that it will be better, more inclusive of those who cannot physically come to our buildings, more focused on what we have found that matters most, and more ready to adapt to our communities with confidence and faith that we can do so.

Out of sacred sadness has come holy hope.

Paul A. Metzler, DMin, is retired from service as a clergy, therapist, educator, administrator, grief counselor, spiritual director, and consultant to community, professional, and religious organizations. Despite retirement, he remains active as a priest associate to several parishes and diocesan-level ministries. Prior to retirement, he was a Fellow in the American Association of Pastoral Counselors; a New York State Licensed Marriage and Family Therapist; a clinical member of the American Association for Marriage and Family Therapy; and active in the Council of Hospice Professionals. He is the book review editor for The Forum, a publication of the Association for Death Education and Counseling, and also for OMEGA—Journal of Death and Dying. He also writes for Journeys, a monthly publication of the Hospice Foundation of America. He and his wife Martie, also a retired priest, moved in 2013 from the northeast to be closer to her family in St. Louis, Missouri.

REFERENCES

The Church News. (1918). Archives of the Diocese of Missouri. Retrieved December 1, 2020 at https://www.diocesemo.org

Huguelet, A. (July 18, 2020). "Dang masks": Parsons derides, shuns face coverings, ignoring top state docs. *Springfield News-Leader.* Retrieved from https://www.news-leader.com/story/news/politics/2020/07/19/coronavirus-missouri-covid-19-masks/5458502002/

The Holy Bible: New Revised Standard Version Bible. (1989). Nashville: Thomas Nelson Publishers.

Metzler, P. (2020). *Considerations for Clergy Ministering to the Sick, At the Time of Death, and The Burial of the Dead in the Age of COVID-19.* Retrieved December 1, 2020 from www.diocesemo.org/files/9415/8757/5196/pastoral_resources_in_the_time_of_covid-19.pdf

St. Teresa of Avila. *Christ Has No Body But Yours*. Retrieved December 1, 2020 from www.thymindoman.com/christ-has-no-body-but-yours-a-poem/

CHAPTER 13

Funerals in the Age of COVID-19

Kenneth J. Doka

L ewis Mumford begins his classic book *The City in History* (1961) by revealing that the first permanent settlements of humankind were cemeteries. Mumford goes on to share another fascinating fact. Our Neolithic ancestors acknowledged the role of funerals and ritual as significant aspects of coping with loss and grief, returning year after year to sacred burial grounds to inter deceased members of their communities. What was known thousands of years ago holds true today. Throughout much of human civilization, funerals have provided a salve for the wounds of loss. But public health restrictions imposed in the aftermath of the COVID-19 pandemic diminished, if not decimated, that therapeutic comfort, as millions of families and individuals in the United States and worldwide have been forced to delay, forgo, or hold these rites of passage virtually, with only a handful of people physically present.

After summarizing the changes to funerals during COVID-19, this chapter reviews the benefits that funerals have previously offered and the effects that their absence, postponement, or insufficiency amid necessary pandemic public health restrictions may mean for the bereaved. Additional rituals that may be helpful as alternatives to funerals are also suggested.

THE EFFECTS OF COVID-19 ON FUNERALS

As funeral home directors and survivors of loss have been mandated to defer to essential health and safety protocols, the idea of "normal" funeral preparation, participation, and attendance has been turned upside down. When a funeral can be held, requirements of limited attendance have forced families to make uncomfortable decisions about who may attend, creating potential division among family members when support is most needed and expected. Due to the "super spreading" potential of large gatherings, many states and/or counties have limited gatherings, including funerals, sometimes to 10 people or fewer.

Funeral service professionals, overwhelmed by both safety adaptations and by the sheer number of deaths in many locations, have worked hard to respond by attempting to offer creative and viable solutions to maintain the funeral tradition. One of the most common examples employed by funeral homes is the streaming of services live over the internet. Some funeral directors also have found ways to broadcast the funeral to cars in parking lots outside of funeral homes. Obvious advantages exist to such approaches; livestreaming allows the funeral to go on and provides funeral access to a larger audience unconstrained by quarantines, the spread of illness, or anxiety about contracting the COVID-19 virus.

Yet the disadvantages are formidable. Especially for older people or for people in underserved communities, many may not be computer literate, own a computer or smartphone, or have access to the internet. And while online funerals can offer a level of participation and involvement, they clearly do not allow the direct personal connection and intimacy valued by the bereaved. Another option of recording a funeral to share later can offer a sense of the event to those who could not attend, but this option likely offers little direct support to the family.

Some funeral homes use website memorials or guest books, which were available prior to the onset of COVID-19, and many funeral directors and families have found these tools particularly useful during the pandemic. These options allow people to share memories and feelings that can support the immediate family in appreciating the legacies left by the deceased. Having a written record is also important, as comments shared verbally at a funeral may not be fully remembered by families absorbed in the shock of grief. Yet ideally, these shared online memories work best as an adjunct to a traditional funeral rather than a substitute for presence; and as is the case with streaming services, online memorials assume a level of digital literacy and internet access.

Another option that many families are choosing is simply to postpone the ritual or forego it completely. Others have held a small funeral at the time of the death with plans to hold a larger memorial service at a later time. These options are understandable choices and can certainly offer value. But at the time of most need, soon after the death, there remains a possible lack of support, and uncertainty as to when such memorial services will be feasible may add to anxiety related to the loss and the pandemic. At press time, while limitations on gatherings vary from state to state, it is unclear how long it will be before restrictions will be fully lifted.

PSYCHOLOGICAL, SOCIAL, AND SPIRITUAL IMPLICATIONS OF THE PANDEMIC

Funerals, as we have known them pre-pandemic, have provided highly effective ways to cope with loss, and ineffective rituals have been shown to complicate grief (Johnson-Arbor, 1981; Parkes, 1975; Doka, 2016). Thanatologists no longer believe in the concept of closure (Berns, 2011); instead, current thinking stresses the continuing bonds that are retained with the deceased (Klass et al., 1996), as well as the fact that we journey with, rather than end, grief (Doka, 2016). Thanatologists and clinicians acknowledge that the funeral is a significant ritual and can be an important component in the grief process. The absence of a funeral can complicate grief when individuals are deprived of this ritual, a rite that has demonstrated myriad psychological, social, and spiritual benefits for the bereaved.

Psychological Impacts

It is not unreasonable then to prognosticate that the disruption of funerals during the period of COVID-19, along with many other aspects of the pandemic period, will result in an increase in complicated grief (intense grief that dominates one's life and ability to function at pre-loss levels for an extended period), as well as other problematic grief reactions for survivors of all types of deaths. Limitations surrounding funerals have affected not only the loved ones of those who died of the coronavirus, but also the survivors of those who died due to old age, other illness or condition, suicide, or accident. It is significant that the overall death rate in the United States has increased during the pandemic, apart from the more than 340,000 U.S. deaths from COVID-19 at press time (CDC, Dec. 31, 2020).

Research has shown that funeral rituals can be critical in helping grievers cope with a sudden or unexpected loss as they allow a sense of symbolic mastery over death and offer opportunities to complete "unfinished business" (Doka, 1984). While COVID-19 deaths may not be fully unexpected, they can happen with unexpected speed. Because of this reality, as well as quarantines and social distancing restrictions, individuals and families may not be able to have the end-of-life rituals desired and may be deprived of the presence of family and friends.

In addition to symbolic mastery, other psychological benefits that could be derived from funerals may be impaired by these same restrictions. Worden (2018) affirms that one of the major tasks of grief is to accept the reality of the death; funerals serve to confirm that reality. As Rando (1984) points out, it is difficult to deny death when every aspect of the ceremony reinforces that reality. Funeral rituals can include viewing the body, accepting the condolences of others, and witnessing acts of final disposition, such as closing the casket, accompanying the body to a cemetery or crematorium, or other acts prescribed by given cultures that may include sitting shiva or washing the deceased's body.

While the immediate family may still benefit if allowed to participate in some of these rituals during the pandemic, others in the social circle of the deceased who are precluded from attendance do not have these options. The absence of many members of the deceased's intimate network will limit opportunities to reminisce and share stories, impairing the ability of mourners to fully review and find meaning in the life of the deceased.

Funerals confirm the reality of death and give social networks an opportunity for collective mourning. They also offer close survivors the opportunity to "do something" at a difficult and disorganized time, helping them remain busy, focused, and purposeful even in the face of loss. Without the possibility for a funeral, that opportunity is absent, leaving ample time for a sense of aimlessness or rumination.

Social Impacts

One of the more prevalent models of grief is the Dual Process Model, which postulates that effective adaptation to loss involves oscillation between two key grief processes—acknowledging the loss and adjusting to the new life created by the loss (Stroebe & Schut, 1999). Similarly, funerals offer a dual process—oscillation between acknowledging and mourning a death while celebrating a life well lived. The social aspect of funerals reinforces this model.

The social benefits of funerals offer vital support in a time of sadness, but also hugs, kind words, and physical presence. Funerals can offer grievers the opportunity to share feelings and to tell stories that validate the life of the person who died. When funerals occur during the pandemic, the need to wear face masks may hide visible emotions and curtail conversation, obscuring the support so plainly evident when someone can read uncovered faces and hear unrestrained speech.

Funerals are rites of passage, now largely absent during the pandemic. These rites are culturally approved rituals that confirm a change of status. The funeral marks both the transition of the deceased from living to dead and the related transition of the survivors from, for example, spouse to widow/widower. Such ceremonies are critical ways that society acknowledges and confirms these changes in status (Van Gennep, 1960).

Often, if there was a period of illness prior to the death, those in the intimate circle may have been absorbed in caregiving, making them socially isolated. The funeral can serve to reintegrate caregivers into their social circle by reaffirming ties, reestablishing social relationships, and publicly reiterating the change in the mourners' status. During the pandemic's social distancing guidelines, such reestablishment and change of status are challenged by both the lack of a funeral that would bring people together and, even if there is some sort of gathering, the need to stay apart.

The funeral service also allows mourners to reminisce and share memories. This process allows mourners to validate the life of the deceased, another critical part of the grieving process. In reviewing their own memories and in hearing the stories of others, mourners can develop a more fully integrated image of the deceased's characteristics and contributions.

Beyond bereaved individuals, funeral rituals provide societal benefits to the larger community. Funerals are events at which the community gathers to mourn together and offer social support. This component reaffirms that the community grieves together, and, through the presence of caring others, reaffirms that mourners are not alone as they cope with their grief. These types of gatherings also provide the opportunities discussed earlier for the sharing of stories, memories, and reminiscences. Finally, funerals can enhance social support. They do this not only by allowing family and friends to gather and remember; the funeral officiant can address ways that mourners can offer support to one another (Doka, 1982). In addition, many funeral homes offer booklets and pamphlets offering bereavement support.

Spiritual Impacts

The spiritual value of the funeral also may be compromised. In addition to the limitations on attendance at the actual funeral that may have religious significance, some faiths may offer ceremonies to commemorate their deceased members that may involve many members of their faith community. In many Jewish traditions, for example, a minimum number of people need to be present for the Kaddish prayer. In Roman Catholicism, masses, especially anniversary masses, may be offered for the deceased. In many Protestant faiths, All Saints Day is often used to commemorate those who have died, particularly but not exclusively those in the past year. Many faith communities now offer mourners a time to gather during the winter solstice for the Longest Night or a Blue Christmas service that acknowledges grief in the holiday season. These types of gatherings are also most likely to be tightly restricted due to the pandemic.

Funerals are spiritually beneficial, offering an opportunity to provide a spiritual or philosophical interpretation of the death. Funerals essentially provide a way to reflect on the meaning of the death within the community's philosophical or spiritual framework. The familiar rituals of a funeral provide a sense of comfort and continuity even in times of insecurity and unknown change. In whatever manner death and its aftermath might be interpreted within a given spirituality or philosophy, rituals can evoke the reminder of a larger community that transcends the present and the promise of a continuing bond. Some of these benefits accrue to the group as a whole. Funerals allow the community to gather to show both solidarity and support to the other mourners and represent a promise that, even with this death, the faith community survives.

An End to Funeral Enhancement

While generally funerals are therapeutic, there are ways to enhance their effectiveness; however, many of these may be precluded by the restrictions currently in place. Participation enhances the value of funerals for many people. The more individuals have opportunities, within their level of comfort, to be involved in the funeral, the greater the level of benefit to their grief process. Mourners can be pallbearers, readers, ushers, or participate in other ways that have great meaning.

As a Lutheran clergyman, I remember seeing the four-year-old great-grandson of the man for whom I was conducting the funeral wandering at the cemetery. I asked the child if he would like to distribute the flowers that mourners would place on the casket. With great solemnity, he gave each mourner a rose. Later, when I visited the widow, she said her most vivid memory of the funeral was her great-grandson distributing the flowers. To her, it reinforced the image of a loving family now reaching forward four generations.

Personalization also is an effective way to enhance the therapeutic value of funerals (Doka, 1984). Such personalization can include the incorporation of personal photos or artifacts at the viewing, allowing personal stories during the eulogy, and even the playing of favorite music. For example, when a dear friend died from ALS, the closing "hymn" was *Singing in the Rain*. An engineer by vocation, his avocation was a bluegrass musician, and one of his regular gigs was at a flea market. The concert was always advertised as "weather permitting," so as an inside joke, the band always opened with a bluegrass rendition of *We'll Sing in the Sunshine*. When told of his terminal diagnosis, he remarked to his wife that they had learned to sing in the sunshine; now they would have to learn to sing in the rain.

Funerals also can acknowledge multiple identities. Most persons play multiple roles in their lifetimes—family roles, work roles, roles in friendships, and others. Yet mourners may only realize one aspect of an individual's identities. For example, when a colleague, Catherine Sanders died, three eulogists—her daughter, a colleague, and a neighbor—each spoke of the Catherine they knew. I feel sure that learning more about the many lives of Catherine was of benefit to all in attendance.

Therapeutic Rituals Beyond the Funeral

The use of therapeutic rituals (Doka & Martin, 2010) can offer support to grieving families, especially at a time when a traditional funeral is not available. These rituals can be developed for a variety of contexts and allow distinct messages.

Rituals of continuity are rituals that emphasize, even in the midst of loss, that the deceased is still remembered. An anniversary mass, for example, serves as a collective ritual of continuity by marking the ongoing continuing bond to the person who has died. Others may choose a less public ritual, perhaps lighting a candle on the deceased's birthday or on the anniversary of the loss.

Rituals of transition affirm that the griever has entered a new place on the journey through grief. In one case, a mother whose son had died over a year ago was reluctant to move any of his clothes or belongings from his bedroom despite the fact that one of her daughters who was sharing a room with her sister had requested the room. In therapy the mother created a ritual much like a potlatch (a gift-giving ceremony of indigenous people that is practiced in the Northwest Pacific and other communities). She reverently chose the items she wished to keep and moved them to special places in her home. She then distributed the remaining items to family and her son's friends in a joyous celebration of his life. Once the belongings were distributed, her daughter was free to move into the room.

Rituals of reconciliation either ask for or extend forgiveness. One man had reconnected with his biological mother later in life but was torn in his loyalties between her and his supportive adoptive family, who seemed ambivalent about the renewed relationship. When he learned that his biological mother had died, he wrote a letter to her and read it aloud in front of his adoptive family, thanking the biological mom for her sacrifice and assuring his adoptive family of the loving and supportive home they had given him.

Rituals of affirmation offer a complement to rituals of reconciliation, as a way of acknowledging legacies or saying thanks. An example of such a ritual is one in which a young man, who had experienced the loss of his father in his early life, developed a ritual to thank his deceased dad for choosing the boy's godfather and securing the godfather's involvement in his life.

Such activities may be useful ways to restore the therapeutic benefits offered by funerals that are now compromised by the pandemic. As the grief resulting from the impact of COVID-19 continues, the effects of the lack of ritual will continue to become more apparent. The impact may be limited, as suggested by forthcoming work by Stroebe and her associates, who are studying the question of limited rituals, separate from the COVID-19 pandemic. Or perhaps a rise in complicated grief will reaffirm the lessons learned by our Neolithic forbearers: Memorialization of the dead deeply affects the living.

Author's Note: Rando's (1984) book, *Grief, Dying, and Death: Clinical Interventions for Caregivers* includes an exceptional summary of the funerals value that after 25 years remains current. This chapter draws from her work as well as others.

Kenneth J. Doka, PhD, MDiv, is Senior Bereavement Consultant to Hospice Foundation of America (HFA) and the recipient of the 2019 Lifetime Achievement Award from the Association of Death Education and Counseling (ADEC). A prolific author and editor, Dr. Doka serves as editor of HFA's Living with Grief® *book series, its* Journeys *newsletter, and numerous other books and publications. Dr. Doka is a past president of ADEC; a former board member of the International Work Group on Death, Dying, and Bereavement; and an advisory board member to the Tragedy Assistance Program for Survivors (TAPS). He is the recipient of The International Work Group on Death, Dying, and Bereavement's prestigious Herman Feifel Award and ADEC's Award for Outstanding Contributions in the Field of Death Education. Dr. Doka is an ordained Lutheran minister and a licensed mental health counselor in the state of New York. This is Dr. Doka's 28th year of involvement with HFA's* Living with Grief® *program.*

References

Berns, N. (2011). *Closure: The rush to end grief and what it costs us.* Philadelphia, PA: Temple University Press.

Centers for Disease Control and Prevention. (2020). CDC COVID Data Tracker. Retrieved December 31, 2020 from https://covid.cdc.gov/covid-data-tracker/#cases_casesper100klast7days

Doka, K. J. (2016). *Grief is a journey: Finding your path through loss.* New York, NY: Atrium.

Doka, K. J. (1984). Expectation of death, participation in planning funeral rituals and grief adjustment. *OMEGA—Journal of Death and Dying, 15,* 119-130.

Doka, K. J. (1982). The funeral service: Grace in grief. *Currents in Mission and Theology, 9,* 235-238.

Doka, K. & Martin, T. (2010). *Grieving beyond gender: Understanding the ways men and women mourn.* New York, NY: Routledge.

Jacobson, S. H., & Jokela, J. A. (2020). Non–COVID-19 excess deaths by age and gender in the United States during the first three months of the COVID-19 pandemic. *Public Health,* Volume 189, pp. 101-103.

Johnson-Arbor, M. (1981). The effect of bereavement on the elderly. *National Report, 4.*

Klass, D., Silverman, P., & Nickman, S. (Eds.) (1996). *Continuing bonds: New understandings of grief.* Washington, DC: Taylor & Francis.

Mumford, L. (1961). *The city in history: Its origins, its transformation, and its prospects.* San Diego, CA: Harcourt.

Parkes, C. M. (1975). Determinants of grief following bereavement. *OMEGA—Journal of Death and Dying, 6,* 303-323.

Rando, T. A. (1984). *Grief, dying and death: Clinical interventions for caregivers.* Champaign, Il: Research Press.

Stroebe, M., & Schut, H. (1999). The dual process model of coping with bereavement: Rationale and description. *Death Studies, 23,* 197-224.

Stroebe, M., Birrell, J., Schut, H., Anadria, D., Newsome, C., Woodthorpe, K.,…Smith, Y. (forthcoming). Cremation and grief: Are ways of commemorating the dead related to adjustment over time. *OMEGA—Journal of Death and Dying* (in publication).

Van Gennep, A. (1960). Vizedom, M. (Translator). *The rites of passage.* London, UK: Routledge.

Worden, J. W. (2018). *Grief counseling and grief therapy: A handbook for the mental health practitioner* (5th Ed.). New York, NY: Springer.

CHAPTER 14

Voices
Supporting Families During COVID-19: A Funeral Director's Experience

William Villanova

2020 began as a promising year for my colleagues and me. We had developed a dynamic funeral program that would assist us in creating Celebrations of Life for our client families that we believed would be unmatched in our profession. January and February provided us the opportunity to implement these initiatives, and they were met with resounding satisfaction. Each meeting with a family began with the funeral director leading a robust dialogue about their loved one—who they were; what they enjoyed; what they didn't like; how they lived and impacted the lives of their family, their relatives, and friends. Through this dialogue we were able to fully collaborate with each family and use all of our available resources to create a funeral service that was meaningful, dignified, and captured the essence of their loved one.

March began much like the previous months; you could almost say "business as usual." We had no clue what was to happen a few short weeks away. On March 11, 2020, I was attending a two-day meeting at the New York State Funeral Directors Association Headquarters in Albany, NY. While there, the first COVID-19 related death happened in New York City. Our executive board began to closely monitor changing conditions in Manhattan. The governor's office was providing updates as the pandemic grew and quickly gripped the five boroughs.

As concern spread throughout our state, businesses, municipalities, schools, and communities all looked for guidance and answers. Funeral homes and funeral directors were quickly thrust to the forefront as "essential workers" and "first responders." My focus was to return back to my office and be alongside my colleagues at Frank E. Campbell–The Funeral Chapel.

Health, Safety, and Welfare

My immediate concern was the health and safety of my colleagues and their families. I knew that if we remained focused on the welfare of our team we could, through full collaboration, create a plan and implement processes to keep our staff and their families, our client families, and our community, safe.

Were they really going to close the city down? Would we be able to have 100% of our team onsite to respond to the needs of our city? In an attempt to stay ahead and respond to the pandemic, the governor began signing executive orders. Many of these orders had, and continue to have, meaningful and lasting impact on the funeral profession and families who have suffered a loss during the pandemic. One of the governor's executive orders stated that funeral directors, funeral homes, and funeral service professionals were essential workers. So as the city slowed with regular activity, my colleagues and I continued operating with a full complement of staff. We learned how to provide funeral services to our community under many necessary restrictions.

Who are Funeral Directors?

Funeral directors are licensed professionals with degrees in mortuary science. They are educated and understand the laws governing funeral service. Funeral directors comply with rules and regulations set forth by federal, state, and local agencies. Like healthcare professionals, they must complete continuing education credits, adhere to professional standards, and comply with Occupational Safety and Health Administration guidelines and all laws governing funeral service and public health laws.

Ahead of the Curve

For many years, funeral directors have maximized the use of technology to provide exceptional service to our client families, including the recording, livestreaming, and video production of funeral services. Our ability to leverage our existing production services allowed families impacted by the pandemic to view and participate in funeral services virtually, which was helpful and well-received by our client families. Using this technology, we were able to multiply attendance in an attempt to provide some normalcy and a feeling of intimacy and support for the immediate members of each family.

Due to the mortality rate increasing daily, we experienced challenges in funeral service like never before, or at least not in my lifetime. All at once, we had families who suffered a loss and were told to shelter in place, yet at the same time make funeral arrangements under challenging restrictions. We received calls from families from all five boroughs asking for assistance, who were nervous, scared, and angry. Emotions were running high as families were making funeral arrangements during the most difficult time in their lives that was now compounded by the pandemic.

At the peak of the pandemic, the mortality rate was six times that of historic values. Yet hospitals had the same number of morgues, and there were the same number of funeral homes available prior to the pandemic. The increased number of deaths put a strain on the ability of hospitals, nursing homes, the medical examiner, and funeral homes to respond to and care for each deceased person. Hospitals exceeded their capacity to care for the sick and properly maintain care of the deceased, so additional field hospitals were established throughout the boroughs and surrounding suburbs. The Jacob Javits Center and some churches were made into medical facilities; a field hospital was established in Central Park and the U.S. Naval Ship Comfort arrived in New York Harbor to provide extra support.

Caring for the Dead

Throughout the boroughs, medical facilities brought in refrigerated trailers to supplement their morgues that had exceeded capacity. When possible, funeral homes did likewise and even renovated their facilities to accommodate the increasing needs throughout the city. Even with all of this effort, some funeral homes could not immediately respond to calls from families. At this point families were looking for a funeral home to just say, "Everything will be alright; we will bring your loved one into our care and assist you." At some point I was asked by a hospital representative if there was more that funeral homes could do to alleviate the enormous concerns and loss brought about by the growing death rate and the restrictions placed on funeral services for families. My response was, "Asking funeral directors to provide appropriate and meaningful funeral services for all of these families in an expeditious manner is like asking all the doctors and nurses to save everyone's life. It just cannot be done."

Obstacles

Cemeteries and crematories began implementing their own restrictions. Limited hours. Limited days. Limited services. Limited amount of family permitted to attend. At one point it felt as though all the funeral directors and funeral homes were working 24 hours a day for weeks and months on end without the ability to schedule an equal number of dispositions. Although it was due to an abundance of caution, the cemeteries and crematories were slow to respond to the needs of families and funeral directors. Eventually crematories expanded their hours of operation and cemeteries returned to a more traditional schedule, while still remaining very restrictive.

We may never know the true emotional impact to families who have suffered a loss during the pandemic. Parents, children, siblings, and loved ones experienced death and are now going through one of the most difficult times in their life alone. Robbed of the traditional emotional and physical support usually provided by extended family, relatives, and friends, these families are left to grieve and mourn alone. Families wanting or expecting to celebrate and memorialize their loved one's life through sharing meals, receiving flowers, or hearing personal tributes realized they were limited or not available. The ability to invite relatives and friends to a public visitation or funeral service was now prohibited, along with funeral services at places of worship or other public spaces. In some cases, religious leaders were unavailable to provide much needed spiritual support. Places of worship were closed, services restricted, and a majority of spiritual leaders were prohibited from providing funeral services due to government-imposed restrictions. The ability to both grieve the loss of, and celebrate the life of, the deceased was taken away. For the many families who begged for traditional funeral services, we provided the prayers from traditional burial rites even though they could not have the ceremony in their place of worship.

Funeral services look and feel different during the pandemic. Families are having limited funeral services that still retain dignity and meaning. We began with private gatherings, funerals, and memorial services for immediate members of the family at the funeral home. As per health officials, remains can be embalmed and the casket can be open. Options for disposition have not changed; families can choose from burial, entombment, or cremation. Committal services are limited to immediate members of the family at cemeteries. As we had already done, we offer livestreaming and recording of funeral services. Out of necessity, the public now has greater awareness of these capabilities and how it may allow opportunities to enhance the service and include more people virtually. All families are encouraged to, schedule a memorial or service of remembrance in the future. I am confident that after all restrictions are lifted, many families will want to properly celebrate the life of their loved ones. Even now, as the effects of the pandemic begin to subside and the restrictions are reduced, many families are scheduling memorial services for their loved ones and holding traditional funeral services in New York City and throughout the state.

While the death rate from the first wave of the pandemic eventually subsided, the abundance of caution and many restrictions remain. The surge in the death rate has moved to other states as New York City and our nation has experienced civil and not-so-civil unrest. You may ask yourself how this affects funeral service. The answer is simple. Protests, rioting, and looting in neighborhoods, on bridges, and in areas of interest throughout the boroughs can compromise the safety of funeral directors who work around the clock providing funeral services for the same communities. During a recent conversation with the New York Police Department, I asked if there was a protocol to assist funeral directors within areas that are unsafe. Unfortunately, the response was, "No." It wasn't bad enough that the pandemic created an occupational health risk, now the simple act of transferring remains could put you and your colleagues in jeopardy. One conversation stands out as I reflect on this time. I was asked by a funeral director, "Is it mandatory that we complete the transfer of remains immediately when a family calls from an area engulfed in a riot or protest?" I stated that it is our responsibility to respond to all families that need our assistance and that we would do our best to work with all authorities to ensure safe passage for all concerned.

Although we continue to make progress through phased re-opening throughout New York, we are far from being "back to normal." I don't know if we will ever go back to society and life as we knew it prior to the pandemic, but I hold out hope. Our families deserve to have their lives back. All families who have experienced loss deserve to memorialize their loved ones with a meaningful service filled with dignity, honor, and respect that both mourns a death and celebrates a life lived without pandemic restrictions.

William Villanova *is the President of Frank E. Campbell–The Funeral Chapel in New York City, the President of the New York State Funeral Directors Association, and a recipient of the National Funeral Directors Association 2020 Pursuit of Excellence and 2019 Best of the Best awards. Frank E. Campbell – The Funeral Chapel has a rich and magnificent history and is arguably the most well-known funeral home in Manhattan, if not the nation. Villanova is a 25-year licensed funeral director in New York and Connecticut and a member of Hudson Valley Community College Mortuary Science Advisory Board. A leader in his profession, he has dedicated his career to mentoring people from all walks of life throughout their careers. Villanova is well known for implementing and promoting the highest standards in funeral service. He and his wife Sandra live in Westchester, NY, with their three children.*

Index